12·20·77

THE PROTEAN BODY

THE PROTEAN BODY

A Rolfer's View of Human Flexibility

Don Johnson

Illustrated by Charles Ramsburg

HARPER COLOPHON BOOKS
Harper & Row, Publishers
New York, Hagerstown, San Francisco, London

To Ida Rolf,
whose eighty years have lightened
the weight of mankind's burden

THE PROTEAN BODY: A ROLFER'S VIEW OF HUMAN FLEXIBILITY
Text copyright © 1977 by Don Johnson. Illustrations copyright © 1977
by Charles Ramsburg. All rights reserved. Printed in the United States
of America. No part of this book may be used or reproduced in any
manner without written permission except in the case of brief
quotations embodied in critical articles and reviews. For information
address Harper & Row, Publishers, Inc., 10 East 53d Street, New York,
N.Y. 10022. Published simultaneously in Canada by Fitzhenry &
Whiteside Limited, Toronto.

Designed by Eve Kirch Callahan

First edition: HARPER COLOPHON BOOKS, 1977

LIBRARY OF CONGRESS CATALOG CARD NUMBER: 76–15325

INTERNATIONAL STANDARD BOOK NUMBER: 0–06–090552–2

78 79 80 81 10 9 8 7 6 5 4 3

Contents

1

The Hologram

Some years ago in a dream, I went with friends to the Fillmore Auditorium in San Francisco. We were standing in an immense foyer like the lobby of the old Fox Theater, with hundreds of people in a circle watching three women dancing. But the women were like holograms, three-dimensional pictures produced by intersecting laser beams. Although they looked solid, I experienced them as colored, three-dimensional projections in the air in our midst, produced by innumerable projectors surrounding us. The dance was taking place about a foot off the floor.

Our bodies are like the bodies of those three women. At any instant they are the three-dimensional projections of energy from many sources. We are like Homer's Proteus, the ancient god of the sea who could change into water, fire, or anything on the face of the earth. Solidity and fixity are myths. My purpose in this book is to expand the awareness of the limits of the body and of its capacity for change—to communicate that the body *is* change.

"The human body is not a thing or substance, given, but a continuous creation. The human body is an energy system, which is never a complete structure, never static, is in perpetual inner self-construction and self-destruction; we destroy in order to make it new.*

In 1968, I was sitting in my New Haven apartment with Ned Hoke, who was leading a massage workshop at Yale. He mentioned that whenever he felt alone or bored, he would simply turn his awareness toward his legs, which were as filled with energy and beauty as a stormy ocean. I couldn't imagine what he was talking about. My legs felt like solid wooden beams. Seven years later, I know what he means. Journeys of awareness into my ankles, knees, or elbows can be as exciting as trips into wilderness forests. I find strange people, ancient ruins, and spirits of every form.

The body is flexible, a fluid energy field that is in a process of change from the moment of conception until the moment of death. The flesh is not a solid, dense mass; it is filled with life, consciousness, and energy. Although you probably would readily acknowledge this quality of the flesh, is it a conscious, operative reality for you? Are you aware of the forms of life in the hands holding this book and in your rear end touching the surface of your chair, of the movement deep in your skull and your lungs?

This book is based on the assumption that most people experience their bodies as opaque, solid masses that, except for deterioration due to age and accident, are by and large fixed. A major barrier to the fullness of human living is the conception that reality is identical with currently popular assumptions about the nature of reality communicated to us as early as the womb. "I'm easily hurt. That's the way I am. My dad was like that too." "I get angry any time anyone criticizes me. That's the way I am." "I have a scoliosis [curvature of the spine]. It's genetic. My father and grandfather have one too." The destruction of that notion of the real liberates one into an exciting world where one can find out for oneself what is really so. This

* Norman O. Brown, *Love's Body* (New York: Random House, 1966), p. 155.

2

world is filled with the unsuspected, with surprises. The surprise packages to be uncovered in this book are within your skin.

There has been a major onslaught on the popular notion of the real during the past forty years. The revolution in atomic physics, research into the psychology of perception, and developments in philosophical phenomenology and linguistic analysis have done in the theoretical respectability of the "real," the "indubitable," the "changeless," the "solidly there." The lives of Carl Jung and Carlos Castaneda epitomize what has happened during these years. Jung recounts in his autobiography the details of a fifty-year process during which he learned that the "real" is not what he and his culture took it to be. Castaneda spent twelve years with the Yaqui wise man Don Juan Matus learning that what he had accepted as real, solid, and indubitable was based not on experience but on assumptions.

In 1967, I was attending lectures at the University of California at Berkeley given by a British empiricist philosopher from Cambridge. He was making great fun of Descartes, the seventeenth-century French philosopher, who had cast serious doubt on the validity of immediate perception. "Why we all know, of course, that when we're strolling down the mall and see the Campanile, it's there. There's no doubt about its relative height and shape and color." A long-haired, Levi-ed, Indian-shirted student raised his hand: "Hey, man, I've seen that Campanile turn into a red serpent, a black round moon; I've seen it become a tiny worm and a giant sea monster." The professor chuckled nervously and went back to his text.

The widespread use of psychedelic drugs has been a major blow to the dependability of the real. We who knew from our studies of physics that the apparently solid table is largely space filled with countless particles moving at incredibly fast and random velocities, now experience the table that way. The popularity of meditation, the development of biofeedback techniques, and the use of fantasy techniques have made common a type of consciousness that twenty years ago was thought to be the possession of shamans, schizophrenics, and mystics. This consciousness is a direct threat to the popular notion of the real.

There is a pattern in both personal and universal history that is reflected here. Men and women seem first to project themselves outside, using external objects unwittingly to work out the drama within. Then at some point there is usually a recognition that the outer world is teaching something about the inner world, and consciousness returns to itself. There is a constant cycle in our lives of outer activity and research followed by inner realization. Now, although it is both acceptable and even fashionable to speak in some circles about the illusory character of the real, that viewpoint is rarely, if ever, applied to the human body itself.

A forty-five-year-old particle physicist telephoned me one evening to discuss his seventeen-year-old son, who had a serious scoliosis. "I had one at his age—wore a brace and had physical therapy for several years, but now it's become permanent." I wondered at the disparity between the man's scientific world and his commonsense observations. His world of physics is insubstantial and governed at best by probabilities. His commonsense world, on the other hand, is solid and certain. But the permanence of the gross structure of the body is more questionable than the flux of its constituent particles.

To leave the world where the real is what people say, what we've been told, and what is assumed to be true is to enter an immense land of unexplored territory. The fixed worlds of the pre-twentieth-century physicist, of the Freudian cynic, and of Archie Bunker dissolve in the acid bath of heightened awareness.

The passage is not always easy and blissful. It is sometimes filled with darkness and terror. The night before I began writing this book, a client and friend killed herself. She was raised in a traditional way in a fundamentalist religion, married a successful businessman, and became a wife and mother.

Her world did not cohere for her; something was amiss. She spent twelve years in psychotherapy. The reality of her world gradually slipped away and she found herself in darkness. Shortly before she died, she telephoned and told me she could get in contact with absolutely no meaning in life, no reason to live.

Ray is twenty years old, a chemistry major with his eyes set on a Ph.D. He rides horses, swims, and runs every day. His first backpacking trip was when he was eight years old. His body is lean and athletic. For a month, he had been in constant pain and was about to withdraw from college. Visits to several specialists had been of no use. As a last resort, his doctor had sent him to be Rolfed. When I took his medical history, he reported only a slightly cracked ilium (the pelvic bone) the previous year, which "had no effect anywhere else," and that a horse had kicked him in the face. Other than that, he had been in top health, without accidents or diseases, until the previous month.

If I were to have closed my eyes, I might have thought I was listening to a much older man, an accomplished intellectual with great social skills. He presented many pictures of who he was: "I'm the kind of person who . . . " "I just can't see a thing," "I have an incredibly low pain tolerance." His muscular system was like a web of taut piano wires.

As we began to loosen the fascia of the pectoralis major (illustrated on the next page), allowing the breathing to flow more easily, tears came streaming out. They seemed unusually deep and filled with anguish. I commented that he seemed to have had years of painful experience. He replied, "I have been in constant pain since the ninth grade." I asked him what happened at that time. "We were living in Morocco. My parents sent me away to school in Paris. I haven't lived at home since. When I was in Paris, I was hospitalized for a pain like the one I've been having lately. They couldn't figure out what it was."

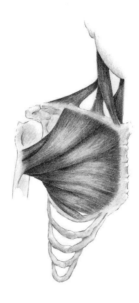

The tears gave way to deep trembling as we loosened the hip joint in the area where he had cracked his pelvis.

Many of us will readily accept the notion that our functioning in the world—our emotions and feelings, our health, the shape of our body, its ease—changes from day to day. But only a rare person lives his life with the feeling that his *structure* is changeable.

There is a bleakness in human life stemming from the assumption that body structure is fixed. In spite of exercise, healthy eating, psychotherapy, and meditation, many of us find ourselves still trapped in old pains, both physical and emotional. Some of us have discovered that the trap often lies in body structure: in the tipped pelvis, the forward neck, the twisted lumbar spine.

A twenty-six-year-old client had successful open heart surgery when she was five. She had enjoyed a basically peaceful and happy life. She was healthy and beautiful, with lots of friends and a satisfying job. She had been in psychotherapy for a long time. When she came for her first Rolfing session, I noticed that her entire body seemed wrapped around the large scar between her sixth and seventh ribs where the surgical incision had been made. During the ten sessions, as we unwrapped this protective system that extended as far as the soles of her feet, seemingly limitless sorrow and tears poured out. There was little content, just tears and sorrow.

Digestion and sexual responsiveness are, for example, among the more basic concerns of life in a body on this planet. Their proper functioning depends on the structure of the body, and this structure is changeable.

A secondary goal of this book is to expand your awareness of the extent to which our bodily behavior is programmed. The way we generally behave in our bodies comes not from an inner sense of rightness and ease, but from the way we were taught to use them and the ways others would like us to use them. A precious possession of our niche in the evolutionary path is our virtually unlimited adaptability. We are capable of innumerable responses to any particular stimulus or group of stimuli. But our adaptive capacity is greatly limited starting in our early months. Our responses become rigidified and predictable until at forty we hear our kids saying, "Oh, I know what he's going to say about that. It'll be the same old story."

The process of nature has worked to create from the world of primates a dancer and an artist; but consciousness has warred with nature to make the dancer-artist into a machine.

We don't like to think we're machines, that all our behavior is patterned and predictable response to the flow of stimuli. We like to think of ourselves as warm, loving, free, and creative beings. Take a closer look. Every time you notice you're getting angry, for example, observe your body. See what parts are usually tight or constricted. Do the same when you're afraid. See if your anger is an individual creative response to a totally new stimulus, or if it is just a recurrence of a trite old pattern. In fact, do you excuse your mechanical response by saying, "But it's the same stimulus—that kid is always breaking glasses"? Wait a minute. That kid is a day older today; she has different feelings and a different awareness. And she's at least broken a different glass.

A rancher friend had a long history of severe accidents in rodeos. These, along with an early polio, had produced a unique twist in his legs, with a resultant unusual style of walking. His twelve-year-old son has the same unique gait even though he has had no accident nor polio.

Performance—for parents, lovers, or audiences—is the great barrier to the creative and adaptive responsiveness that is our natural possession. We need to buy love because we feel threatened and empty. And we're willing to pay any price even if it means giving up our soul to become a machine.

Ray came for his second session of Rolfing three days later. He spoke lightly of the excruciating pain after his first session. His chest was sore and his back pain had been unbearable. When I asked if anything else had happened, he reported that he had stopped taking codeine and aspirin for the first time in a month and was taking long walks every day. He complained about the S-curve in his spine, saying that he was the only one in his family who wasn't "straight." The S-curve was not, in fact, unusually pronounced and it was dramatically reduced by his allowing his breath to open his upper chest, causing his head to rise upward.

As I began working on his feet, I noticed that they seemed to be marked by the compression characteristics of feet that at an early age have been put into orthopedic shoes. "Oh, yes. Everyone in my family has worn orthopedic shoes. But I wore them only until I was five years old. I don't know why." "Oh, by the way," he continued, "I just remembered that this huge two-hundred-fifty-pound man stepped on my foot at a reception on my first day at school in Paris. It was badly twisted." Five weeks later he told me the man was not very big at all.

While we continued to work, I asked him if he ever spent time just being with himself. "Yes. All the time. I can shut absolutely everything off outside me." "No, I mean can you just be with yourself without having to do anything or feel you have to think about something?" "Oh, no, I always have to be doing something or thinking about something." I suggested that he spend ten minutes each day resting on his back, letting the breath take over and just watching what happens.

Everybody knows that the body changes. You eat too much, your pants get tighter, and you've got to go up to another size. A few months later, your new pants are baggy and you can't wear them. As you approach forty, you start limping. Your daughter breaks her leg and she can't run quite as fast as she used to. She even complains a lot about pains in a new way. Flesh gets pimply, clears up, becomes hard, dry, and wrinkled with age. Blood circulation increases when you improve your diet or take up a new exercise program. Your height even changes during adulthood, usually shortening as you grow older, but sometimes increasing if you come out of a severe depression—or take a ride on a spacecraft.

I'm not here to tell you that the body changes. You already know that. What I'm saying is that it changes more than you suspect, and it's changeable in ways more radical than you suspected.

There are several approaches to changes in the body. Medical science and technology represent a vast industry whose aim is to produce changes in the body. Health spas, diet ranches, yoga classes, and athletic training camps rely on the plasticity of the body.

The specific viewpoints I will consider are:

1. *Personal history.* Your body represents your unique history, including the way your parents taught you to use your body by the way they

used their own bodies. It also includes birth experiences—often traumatic—accidents, illnesses, and your particular emotional history in its relation to your flesh.

2. *Culture*. Your unique form is the distinct realization of more universal patterns which themselves are in an almost imperceptible state of change. The image of female beauty is communicated from the earliest years through the media: the posture of fashion models, of movie stars, of singers and playmates. The same is true for men. The athletic male, the Marlboro man, and the sexy movie hero set the standards in comparison with which we feel good or bad about our own bodies. Morphological evolution is also a factor. One day I asked a client (illustrated here) why he did sit-ups when his body was so tight, especially his ulcerous belly. He replied

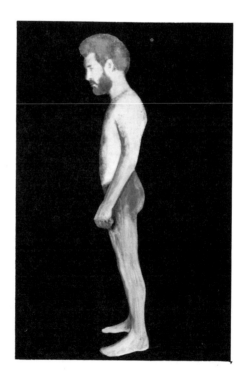

that he wanted to look like certain males whom he admired. They looked straight and handsome to him. I pointed out that they were not tall and open, but that their heads, like his, were pulled forward by the shortness of muscles in the front. What we see is a function of our unique place in the evolutionary path. What a Greek of the Golden Age sees as straight and open, a twentieth-century bioenergetic therapist would consider tight and closed.

3. *Gravity*. We are subject to the same laws as any physical form. Moving throughout life in the field of gravity puts strains on us that we deal with in ways that are both unique and patterned. The form our body has at any particular time is a function of those static and dynamic force vectors.

4. *Intention*. What we intend to do with ourselves literally shapes us: how we choose to deal with our environment, our fears and other emotions; the types of activity we choose; the life-style we create; the food we eat; our programs of exercise and stress reduction.

The notion of structure is crucial in this book. Here's how I use it. As you're sitting reading this book, you are in a certain *posture*, possibly leaning against the back of a chair, your head forward, much of your weight on your right hip, your head canted to your left, and your arms resting comfortably on your lap. Now stand up—or visualize yourself doing so—trying to become as vertically comfortable and balanced as you can. Check places where you feel tight or uncomfortable or just opaque. If you really want to get into this experiment, observe yourself in a full-length mirror or have someone take a photograph of you. You'll find that there are some places that seem too short or tight—the backs of the legs, the small of the back, the groin, the back of the neck. You are now becoming aware of your *structure*.

Structure refers to the relatively stable relation of large body segments (head, torso, pelvis, legs, feet) to one another. The relations are a function of the length and tone of muscles, fasciae, tendons, ligaments, cartilage, and bones. If you have a photograph of yourself standing up straight in a bathing suit when you were twelve and now look at your forty-year-old body, you might find, for example, that both then and now there is a slight twist in your shoulders, the right one pulled back further than the left, and a similar twist in an opposite direction in your hips. Perhaps you've been told by a physician that you have a scoliosis, or by a chiropractor that your fifth lumbar is rotated. Those are all matters of the way you *are* bodily. Posture refers to what you do with all that as you move through life. As its Latin root, *ponere,* suggests, posture is the way you place yourself—as you're now doing, sitting and holding this book.

Structure and posture are obviously related. If you have a rotation in the vertebrae of your neck, you might find it more comfortable to have your head and eyes more frequently rotated to the right. Because structure makes one posture more comfortable than another, it makes us predictable, contributing to our transformation into machines. If you're tight on one side of your body, you will generally sit so as to alleviate the feelings of tightness. If you watch a solo dancer or a runner, you'll notice certain unbalanced patterns of movement: the dancer will often make strong dramatic moves to the left but rarely and with less grace to the right; the runner will flow more smoothly as he brings his left leg forward than as he brings his right.

Posture also feeds into structure. A tennis player will, over the years, find his right shoulder becoming significantly different from his left. A person who spends a good deal of her childhood slouching in an easy chair reading in poor light and later goes on to become a scholar will find herself with the characteristic stooped shoulders, sunken chest, and drooping head.

These considerations of the variability of body structure have broader implications. As our perception of our fundamental physical being becomes more flexible and differentiated, our relation to larger areas of human concern also changes. The later chapters of this book discuss the impact our experience of body structure has on politics, spirituality, and intimate personal relationships.

I had to schedule Ray for three sessions in five days because his intense pain had forced him to leave school and I wanted to see how far we could bring him. He came for his third session, the day after his second, looking much happier and lighter. He had spent the day working in his parents' stable, shoveling hay, riding, and taking a long walk. His back had improved so much that he was planning to return to school the next day. Following my suggestion to spend time with himself, he had lain down that day and immediately fallen asleep.

I worked mainly on the area between his lower ribs and the top of his pelvis. He responded beautifully, working with me, allowing his breath to flow. We took pictures at the end of the session that revealed how much he had expanded both laterially and vertically in the course of the three sessions. He felt very light, with lots of energy along the back of his head. We parted for the week.

2

The Anatomy of Plasticity

The purpose of this chapter is to question the currently popular conception of the nature of the body and to communicate some information about this basic matrix whose states of change I will discuss in subsequent chapters.

When you get a headache, do you think it's a problem with your head, or rather, do you feel in your guts it's a problem with your head, even though you might have read or been told that headaches are due to nervousness? When you contract an ulcer, do you think the problem is in your belly? Does it occur to you that your headache or ulcer may be part of a complex that involves a tipped pelvis, limited sexual responsiveness, sexual frustration, and anger?

There is a profound error in the popular conception of the body, most strongly supported by modern medicine. The error consists in putting primary consciousness on parts and secondary awareness on the whole system.

My eleven-year-old daughter, Rina, was taking a fifth-grade anatomy class. Her first test was on the assignment to learn the names of all the bones, then the muscles, then the organs, and on through the various parts of the body. My wife, Elissa, a teacher of Structural Patterning, volunteered to teach one of the anatomy classes. She had the kids feel their bodies, paying special attention to being aware of specific kinds of muscular action. She had them focus on parts of their bodies as they walked and sat. She had them feel, internally and with their hands, what happened to their bodies when they breathed. The teacher was very pleased, saying, "What an unusual approach!"

Medical students learn about the body in the same way that fifth-graders do. They just learn more answers.

There are at least two problems with this method. One is the illusion that this particular approach to the body is a picture of reality: that the body is a collection of relatively independent but interacting systems. The second problem is that, once you have lost the wonderment and sense of unity about the whole body that was part of the origins of the system, you and all the king's men can't really get the parts together again. The unity was there at the beginning; it doesn't have to be constructed. The so-called systems of the body are only viewpoints to clarify questions about the original unity.

Knowledge has its origins in wonderment, in the questions we ask about phenomena that puzzle us. Our questions give rise to opinions, conjectures, theories—all more or less true or probable or maybe even just slightly possible. Over the centuries, certain kinds of questions and the various attempts to answer them are grouped together into what we call a branch of science. Galileo, the father of the analytical thought forms that persist in modern medicine, began by puzzling over the rhythm of the swinging sanctuary lamp in the nave of the Duomo in Pisa. Abbé Mendel fathered modern genetics by spending years watching the color patterns in the flowers of pea plants. Vesalius and Leonardo da Vinci wondered about the complexities of human movement and gave birth to anatomy.

With few notable exceptions, elementary schools, high schools, and professional schools fail to teach the process leading from question to possible answer. They teach instead the contemporary answers as *knowledge,* as the picture of what is so. Rina, for example, was being taught that the body *is* that particular collection of fragmentary systems described in contemporary anatomy books, when in fact that view is just one explanation of the phenomenon of the human body.

The Frankenstein myth summarizes the illusion in the medical model of the body. Dr. Frankenstein thinks he can put together a man because medicine has taught him that a man is an "incredible machine." If you can get all the parts, put them together properly, then shoot it up with energy, you'll have a man.

This crude view of the body is an unconscious result of the origins of modern science in the seventeenth century centering especially around Galileo and Descartes. Galileo shocked the Christian world by opposing the telescope to the Bible. Descartes added to that shock by eliminating from the field of cognitive reliability the subjectivity of human perception and feeling. The stage was set for the development of modern science in their agreement that the only kind of reliable knowledge is based on the exact measurement of matter in motion, purged of human perception, emotions, and values.

In the seventeenth century, as well as now, there was a need for experience to be liberated from established dogma and commonsense opinions about the indubitable nature of the real. But the error occurred in making a shift from liberation to metaphysics: the construction of a model of reality, specifically of human reality, based on the distinction between mind and matter.

The model of the body I am discussing is a relic of that period. The history of physics and chemistry, developments in psychology and philosophy, have all come to recognize the inadequacy of that model. But popular thought and medical thought have not yet caught up—or gone back far enough.

Ray came for a fourth session a week after he'd had his third. He'd had two days of residual pain following the three Rolfing sessions. He returned to school, where he had a lot of work to make up, and began to experience

16

the old pain on his left side. On Wednesday, he had blacked out and fallen down a flight of stairs. He reported that at least he had been able to take a long vigorous walk every day. "Sometimes, after a mile, I experience intense pain, but I keep on going for another four." I advised him to listen to his body, to let it educate him. He laughingly replied that he had always driven his body, but he was able to understand what I said about listening to it. He also reported how much he was enjoying spending time with himself, just lying and breathing, each day.

He was very upset, however, about his changed relation to other people. "I used to be like a turtle. I was always inside my shell, not liking other people, not wanting to relate to them. I started changing in high school. I began to enjoy people. But now I'm back where I started. I don't like to be with people." I asked him if it made any sense to think of being with people the way he was with himself in those short periods each day, just hanging out with them—the way he was right then. "Oh, no. I always want to do something for them. That's the way I am." I asked how he felt when someone hung out with him just the way he was, sad, happy, depressed, or whatever. "I like that. That would mean he trusted me."

A general goal of the first seven sessions of Rolfing is to modify your present body structure: to remove old stress patterns, old postures, old ways of bodily relating to the world. But whatever happens on one level of personal existence is reflected on all levels. During the early sessions of Rolfing, people frequently report that they feel disoriented, freaked out, unfamiliar in their world, unable to relate to people as they did in the past. Some refer this "taken-apart–ness" to their body: they fall down a lot, they throw out their backs doing heavy work in old ways. They often report feeling like newborn babes.

To understand what often happens during the Rolfing process, I find an ancient way of analyzing human existence useful. It is based on the availability to each of us of three qualitatively different experiences of ourselves: (1) In what are for most of us rare experiences, we are aware of ourselves as connected with the universe, as appropriate, as fitting and worthwhile just as we are. This has traditionally been called our essential self that is revealed in what we now call "peak experiences"—mystical states and moments of artistic insight and creativity. At the specifically bodily level, it is feeling good, easy, mobile, with full use of our energy. (2) Another level of self-experience is the awareness of our deep inadequacy. This is the level of self-doubt, depression, and despair. In the body, it is the level of the deepest hurts, distortions, and scars. (3) A more common level of experience is of the self we show to the world in everyday life. It is constructed to hide the self-hating feelings of the second level, which themselves are born of forgetfulness of our essential selves. At this level, we pretend that everything is OK when we actually think it isn't. We hide our anger and hostility. We are polite and manipulative. In the body, it is the level of muscular imbalances used to shield us from experiencing the deeper discomforts.

Each of us experiences all these levels at one time or another. One level, however, characterizes our fundamental relation to life at any particular period. The third level is most common, but there are periods of depression, psychotic episodes, and attacks of anxiety. Some of us spend most of our lives at the second level, usually in hospitals. Only rare human beings find themselves habitually at the first level.

The levels are reflected directly in the body and in what happens during the Rolfing process. Ray, for example, presents a set of postures to the world. The average eye would see him as healthy, filled with vitality, joy, and energy. But his outward use of his body is constructed to hide the misery he has been feeling all these years. Rolfing proceeds by stripping him of the veil of muscular compensations to get to the real misery, so that finally we can reach a level of bodily existence where there is ease and a maximum of energy without effort.

It should be noted that this three-fold division is not intended as a "picture" of the person, but as a tool to unlock the doors of our experience. It seems useful, for example, to realize that many of us have protected ourselves from feeling the pain of serious accidents we've had. As we begin opening our bodies to move to a more energetic level, there is often a recurrence of the original pain we've been avoiding. A thirty-year-old woman had a serious back injury when she was fifteen years old, followed by chronic low-grade back pains. After her first session of Rolfing, she felt the pain with the same intensity she had originally experienced. My goal in working with her was to bring her body to a freer level of functioning than would be possible if she continued avoiding that experience. One of my goals was to deal with the deep distortion originating in the accident that had led to the series of compensations.

There are many alternative viewpoints to the popular view of the body as an incredible machine made up of many parts. The Chinese system with its acupuncture meridians, and the Indian system with its chakras, are based on centuries of observations of uniform channels of energy flow throughout the body. In the West, there is the alchemical model of the body based on the principle of harmony between microcosm and macrocosm.

The matrix for the phenomenon I'm considering is that system of the body which arises from the mesoderm, a primitive layer of cells that occurs in one of the earliest differentiations of the fertilized ovum. It includes fasciae, muscles, tendons, ligaments, cartilage, and bones. The relationship among these elements forms what I call the structure of the body. They determine how a person's body is and how he functions. They determine the relative positioning and functioning of the other elements of the body: the nervous system, the circulatory and digestive systems, the lymphatics, the respiratory system. With the exception of muscle tissue, all tissues are composed of the same basic stuff: protein fibers called collagen, elastic fibers, reticular fibers, and a gelatinous medium. One type of tissue, say, a tendon, differs from another, say, a bone, in the relative proportion of these components.

Fascia is the forgotten organ of the body. It starts just below the surface of the skin to form an inner covering for the entire body. At certain places where body function demands it, it thickens to form bracelets to stabilize tendons at joints such as the ankles and wrists, or to form large sheets called aponeuroses. The accompanying illustration shows how in many people the superficial fascia of the forearm thickens at the wrist. In other places it dives deeper to connect with another layer of fascia that also covers the entire body at this deeper layer. In the embryo, individual muscle fibers develop within the bed of fascia, forming a muscle bundle as a group of fibers appears within a single fascial sheath.

Fascia is a primary vehicle for changes in the body—for good as well as ill. A severe leg fracture, for example, will cause the fascia in that area to become like gristle. This "knot" inhibits the free movement of the neighboring muscles. In other places, lack of use or poor posture will give rise to shortening of fascial planes and adhesions of those planes to muscles and bones, also limiting body movement and the flow of fluids through the flesh. In many places, such as the bottom of the buttocks, the fascial covering of one muscle group (the gluteal muscles) will become confused and enmeshed with the covering of another group (the hamstrings), resulting in restricted movement through the area.

Here is the classical view of the fasciae: "The fascial planes of fasciae really constitute, in the non-dissected condition, a sheet of connective tissue varying in thickness and density according to locality. This covers and invests all the so-called higher structures, i.e., muscles and tendons, bursae, vessels, lymph nodes, nerves, viscera, ligaments, joints, and even cartilage and bones, these last by close adhesion to perichondrium and periosteum between the attachments of the muscles."*

This quote is from the only book ever done on the nature of fascia, except for an expansion by Gallaudet's pupil, Edward Singer. And yet fascia is the unifying organ of the body. It is the matrix for the flow of metabolites, for circulation, and for nervous flow. Shortening and thickening of fascia distorts the whole body. By loosening and moving the fascia, you can radically alter the body.

We have been seduced by our language to think of aspects of the body as separate parts attached to each other. But if you take a close look, for example, at the attachment of the pectoral muscle via its tendon to the humerus of the upper arm (see illustration on page 6), you will not find a series of separate parts joined together. Toward the end of the muscle, itself a bundle of fibers in a bed of fascia, there appears a thickening of

* B. B. Gallaudet, *A Description of the Planes of Fascia of the Human Body* (New York: Columbia University Press, 1931), p. 1.

the fibers gradually flowing into what we call a tendon, which begins to fan out again, flowing into what we call the periosteum, or fascial covering of the bone, which is, microscopically, indistinguishable from the bone itself.

Body structure is actually a functional differentiation of the same primary material. At places of extreme stress, there is a thickening of the tissue in which what are called collagen tissues become more dense. In places where there is a need for rigidity, the blood supplies calcium salts and you have bone. In other places, there is a need for the flexibility of soft muscle invested in fascia.

"If the myofascial system is considered as a functional whole rather than as a merely additive complex of tissue, it becomes apparent that this is the organ of support—a resilient unitary fascial framework which initiates, transmits, and determines movement, as well as ensheathing and supporting all individual parts. Muscles work as interconnected, balanced systems, not as individual motors for body parts. They are physiologic systems rather than anatomic elements. The myofascial system and its related neural mechanisms determine spatial movements of joints and thus the direction and quality of all movement. In turn, movement acts as a pumping mechanism; in this way, the myofascial system is an important factor in fluid exchange at all levels of the organism. Anatomically, the myofascial system thus has a part in determining metabolic levels in local areas as well as in the body as a whole. It so becomes a vital factor in the bioenergetic regulation of the body and its homeostatic and thermodynamic equilibrium."*

I was once working with a thirteen-year-old boy who had Osgood Schlatter's disease, a mysterious inflammation of the bone and connective tissue at the insertion of the rectus muscle of the thigh just below the knee cap. It caused him such pain that he had to give up all sports. He lived on a ranch several hours from Santa Fe, so it was difficult for him to get to my office. As I attempted to accelerate the Rolfing process, I reverted to my old myopic approach to the body, giving primary attention to his legs. One day,

* Ida Rolf, "Structural Integration: A Contribution to the Universtanding of Stress," *Confinia Psychiatrica* 16 (1973): 71.

my wife, Elissa, pointed out to me that his head was so far forward that he had to strain the rectus muscle to keep himself erect while he was walking. He and I spent the whole session lengthening and restructuring his neck so that he could rest more comfortably on top of his shoulders. He has experienced no pain in his knee in the year since.

The divisive kind of thinking that is our heritage from Descartes and his followers literally goes right into our marrow. While it's useful to make distinctions between various parts of the body, just as it's useful to make distinctions between emotions and physiological phenomena, errors occur when we think of those distinctions as pictures of reality. Because of the seductive structure of our language, we feel there is such a *thing* as an emotion, another *thing* that is the nervous system, and another *thing* that is a tight muscle. The person is like a plant whose fibrils, nearly indistinguishable from their nourishing soil, flow into the roots that flow into the trunk that differentiates into branches and leaves and flowers and beyond into the electrical field surrounding it. Spiritual consciousness, emotions and feelings, intelligence, physiochemical functioning, the musculoskeletal systems, are all only viewpoints from which we can examine the single reality we are.

Notice that the very stuff we are made of is highly elastic. The composition of all the connective tissues of the body is the same. The tissues vary according to their degree of elasticity, ranging from relatively inelastic bones to the extremely elastic fascial wrappings of muscle fibers.

"Hey, what about bones? They're solid." "My back is badly curved, but I guess there's nothing I can do about that. It's in my spine."

"The dry, rigid, bare bones of the macerated skeleton belie the qualities of living bones. These are clothed in a vascular membrane, the periosteum, with numerous blood vessels at their ends; endowed with resilience readily shown by the spring of a clavicle or by the compression and release of a chicken's wishbone; capable of effecting the most serious fracture repairs till the bone is like new and of adjusting the fine architecture of their structure to meet new stresses. . . ."*

These elastic members of body structures form a network capable of change. Consider the possibilities for movement, adjustment, distortion, and change at the joints.

First there are the more common joints, of which most people are aware: elbows, wrists, knees, ankles, hips, and so on. At each of those places, as you've undoubtedly been aware when you've sprained one, there is much possibility for change.

A less commonly recognized system of joints occurs in the feet and hands. There are twenty-eight bones in the foot, with thirty-two joints. Now just think of all the possibilities of change in such a structure. There are twenty-seven bones in the hand and thirty-two joints.

* Robert D. Lockhart, *Anatomy of the Human Body* (Philadelphia: Lippincott, 1972), p. 11.

The spinal column has 134 movable joints, *not* counting the interverte-bral disks. Each of the upper ten ribs has two places where it is free to move: at its vertebral attachment in the back and at its attachment in the front via cartilage either to the sternum or to the costal arch.

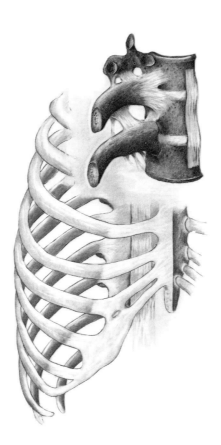

"But at least there's fixity in the pelvis and the skull." Hell, no. You can't find fixity anywhere. There are three joints in the pelvis: one right in the middle of the pubic bone, and the two sacroiliac joints. Several body specialists have discovered that those joints can be kept mobile throughout adult life with proper manipulation, breath, and body movement.

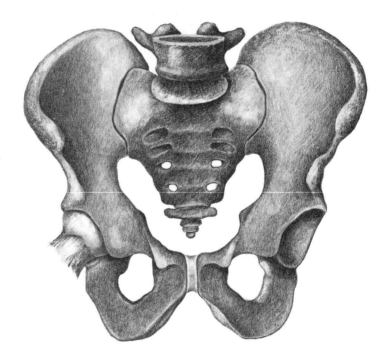

There are sixteen bones in the skull, not counting the jawbone. William Sutherland, a disciple of Andrew Still, the founder of osteopathy, discovered that the nearly fifty joints in this structure, all of which are movable in the infant, can with proper manipulation continue to move throughout the average person's life.

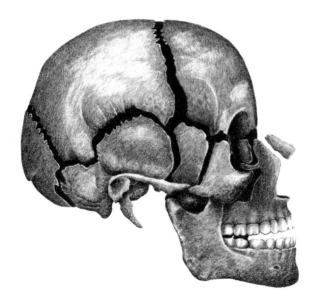

So there's your solid bony structure: hundreds of elastic bones each of which can be distorted by pressure, fractured, deflected, straightened, twisted. All of them are put together with hundreds of joints at each of which infinite kinds of movement can occur along with dislocation, twisting, and readjustments. This is the most stable component of our protean body.

The other aspect of body structure—the cartilaginous components of joints, the ligaments that bind the joints together, the tendons that unite the muscles to the system, the omnipresent fasciae—are even more elastic and subject to change by stress, accidents, stretching, straining, and manipulation.

What is remarkable is that we look today so much the way we did last week. From the moment our mother's ovum was fertilized until now, the ground substance of our being is in constant flux and alteration and will continue so until we die.

3

Personal History

At this moment, your physical form is the unique result of your personal history: parents, gestation and birth, home environments, accidents, illnesses, the ways you learned to use your body. Your flesh is your family album, your personal diary.

Katerina is a beautiful, tough seventy-four-year-old Bostonian who homesteaded in Oklahoma in 1945. True to her Yankee tradition, she had never indulged in any of the emotional "therapies." But taking care of her hundred and twenty acres with its orchards and huge vegetable garden was getting tiring. Some of her younger friends suggested Rolfing. She had also developed a large growth in her abdomen. Her doctors could find no signs of malignancy, nor could they locate the tumor. Her physician also suggested Rolfing. Her well-toned, well-used flesh responded promptly to the work.

In her first session with me, she mentioned that she had always been the tallest girl in her classes in high school and college. Since she was considerably shorter than my 5 feet 9½ inches, I felt the female form must indeed have evolved upwards. After our fifth session, however, she emerged from the table slightly taller than I. She was beginning to look like the tall, graceful lady she must have been.

That evening, in her sleep, her mother appeared to her, placed her hand on her belly, and said, "Now you can have cancer too, Katie, just like I did." She spent the whole next day sobbing, recalling how at twenty years old she was the only one in the family who would take care of her mother, who was dying of cancer. She resented it, hating the smell and the mess. She felt guilty for her resentment when her mother finally died.

During the entire day after her seventh session, during which I worked on her neck and head, she found herself watching a movie of her entire life. She relived her birth, saw herself in her crib, and experienced scenes from infancy.

During this chapter, let your mind wander back through those years, remembering the house or apartment in which you lived as an infant, the ways your parents looked, the clothes you all wore. Get out some old pictures and look at their bodies and at your body and its earliest manifestations.

"The newborn baby is not at all the unconscious little thing we have assumed it to be for such a long time. We assumed that a newborn baby doesn't feel, doesn't see, doesn't hear, has no emotions. It is just the opposite. . . . A baby still has a consciousness which is wide open, not conditioned, and this is what is making birth so traumatic. This consciousness is unprotected and fully opened. The baby takes in everything without discrimination."*

Personal history might begin something like this: I find myself in a dark, cozy, soft atmosphere. Things are extremely pleasant except for some occasional noise outside, the sounds of Mom and Dad fighting with each other about something. Also, I'm beginning to experience some nervous

* Frederick Leboyer, interview in *New Age Journal,* no. 8 (October 1975), pp. 15–16.

vibes in the atmosphere. Mom's getting a little scared of the whole thing. That makes me a little scared too. Suddenly, just as things have gotten very tense and scary, I find myself yanked out into a cold room with blinding lights and a lot of strange people dressed in white. I sense that Mom, though semiconscious, is experiencing terrible pain and fright. I almost killed her. What kind of monster am I?

So I get swatted on the ass while suspended from my heels, and carried off alone to a room filled with a bunch of yowling things like myself. Once in a while I get a warm breast that feels really good. But I'm feeling a little haggard from the experience. I've already got some tension in my body. The noise and nervousness that penetrated my mom's womb made me curl up a little tighter to shield myself from those vibrations. In that awful delivery room, I tightened up my neck in the midst of all my yelling.

In a few days, I get carried home from the hospital to my grandpa's house, where Mom and Dad are living. Things aren't good here. Mom and Dad don't get along well. Dad isn't home very much. He works hard and then spends a lot of time with his men friends. Mom's not too happy with Grandpa because he is about as helpless as I am. So here she is with three males burdening her life. Hey, what am I getting into? Sometimes I yowl when I'm wet, hungry, or uncomfortable. Mom gets worried. I don't want to worry you, Mom, I just want some food. Sometimes I just smile, being completely open to them. They don't know how to handle that at all. They play a lot of silly goo-goo games with me. I begin to understand games I can play to get affection and attention from them. So when I want something, I look real cute or I scream my bloody head off. I'm becoming convinced that life is a pile of shit and the only way to deal with it is to cover it over with a lot of games. I'm also learning that *being* is not where it's at if I want to get a lot of warmth and attention. So at six weeks old, I've decided to live a life of self-deception, gradually forgetting who I really am. And, by God, I'm going to use my keen little mind to prove I'm doing the right thing.

This book is about the radical changeability of the ground of our being, the understanding of which leads to exciting new possibilities for life. The deepest block to this kind of understanding is the world view that you, like me, developed so far back you've forgotten it was a viewpoint and came to confuse it with reality. The viewpoint, which in my experience is fairly standard, is something like this: Life from its miserable beginning to its miserable end is basically a pile of shit. We can deal with it by just giving in to it, which doesn't work because it's too miserable. Or we can cover it over with pretense. Or if we are sophisticated intellectuals, the Freudian heirs of the Greek and Roman Stoics, we can accept it without being disturbed by it, consciously adapting to a life of suffering without being deluded by false hopes.

The real hooker, though, is that we've put so much investment into the viewpoint that we're more interested in proving that it's right than in experiencing the possibility of a more satisfying existence.

I'm four years old. My funny old Swedish grandma is taking care of me during the afternoon. I get mad at her for something or other. I go out into the kitchen, get a butcher knife, and chase her. She runs out the back door, hooks it, locking me inside. I hook the inside latch and cleverly run out the front door around the back. As I'm rounding the corner of the house in the back, I run smack into my mother with that same look of horror on her face. She takes the knife away and spanks the hell out of me. I recently asked her what she was feeling then. "I've raised a monster!" she replied.

Early in my life I learned the skills to use anything and anyone, from my parents, to Sister Vincent, to Father Wall, to Carl Rogers and Ida Rolf, to prove that I was a monster, incapable of living a joyful, satisfying, and creative life.

The world is a teacher. If I had been able to listen to the world's feedback instead of attempting to prove to the world that I was right, I would have learned that responses that may have been useful when I was in the womb, like tightening my chest, are no longer useful. They cause me pain, inhibit my breathing, and have given me years of asthma.

"In a random body, any given movement evokes response not only from the muscle primarily concerned (and its antagonist), but from a chorus of other units as well. Some of this accompanying group may interfere with, or limit, the movement, rather than support it. The resulting aberrated flow may, in fact, be an inversion of the movement demanded. It is a jangle of responses, altering or even inverting the movement intended. Originally, these compensatory restrictions may well have been an effort to support on the part of the body, an attempt at 'splinting' or 'relieving' an injured part. But at the present time, they are barriers to movement; circumventing their restriction demands exhausting outpourings of energy."*

In the well-ordered body there is also response throughout the whole body to the activation of any individual muscle group, but the response is harmonious and supportive. As I write or play the piano, there is, besides the specific movements in hands and forearms, rhythmic response deep in the pelvis continuing right through the insides of my feet.

The Catholic Church entered my life at an early age. Of course, one of the first things I learned was the teaching about hell, even though it was hardly ever mentioned. Wow, the idea of burning with your body for all eternity! When I was about four, I asked Mom what heaven was like. She said it's whatever you want most. I was just getting over the flu and what I most wanted was hamburgers and milkshakes. Now just compare the power of a vision of eternal hamburgers and milkshakes with the vision of physically burning forever. Hell got into my gut, my dreams, and my imagination in a way that heaven never did. I would go to sleep at night worried that I might end up some day in that frightful place. And it was easy to get there, I thought. All you had to do was tell a bad lie or be disobedient or steal a large amount of cookies. Later on, it got even easier to get to hell. All you

* Ida Rolf, "Structural Integration: A Contribution to the Understanding of Stress," *Confinia Psychiatrica*, 16 (1973): 73.

had to do was touch your genitals affectionately or look in the mirror at your naked body with pleasure.

So I grew up careful not to end up there. Pictures of me from my earliest years up until around thirty reveal that same tight, smiling face, a solid mask, careful not to let the inner devil emerge. And I surrounded my pelvis with so much armor that it took my Rolfer, Ed Maupin, two hours just to loosen a few adductor muscles at the bottom of my pelvis.

The hook was, of course, that I was already convinced in my deepest being that I was a monster and that I would probably go to hell even if I was careful. So I spent most of my life playing the good boy, while behind the scenes, never confessing them, I was paving my way to hell with boyhood lies, adolescent masturbation, and then really doing it up big by having an affair with a married woman while I was a Jesuit priest, then marrying a divorced Jewish woman. I had committed such serious sins that only the delegate of the pope himself could forgive me.

I once asked Father John, my fourth-grade catechism teacher, this question: Say I've committed a mortal sin (one that makes you worthy of burning forever in hell. There are two ways you can be absolved of a mortal sin: the first, certainly impossible for a monster like me, is an act of perfect love for God and sorrow because of that love; the second, when you're sorry just because you don't want to burn forever, is to confess your sin to a legitimate priest and have him absolve you). I go to confession, sorry for my sin just because I'm afraid of going to hell. Unbeknownst to me, there sits in the dark confessional box an imposter. I confess my sin to him and he pretends to absolve me. I leave the church, am immediately struck by a car, and die. Where, Father, do I go, heaven or hell? Without the least bit of hesitation, Father John responded, "Hell."

My body pattern reflects those early teachings: extreme tension keeping it all together, keeping the supposed demonic power from erupting; afraid that it will erupt at any minute, so putting a lot of energy into holding it all in place: the anger, the rage, the sexual feelings, the panic. In fact, hell was always more interesting to me than heaven. The good life, holding everything in, seemed boring, so I always saw to it that I kept secretly along the path to letting the demonic finally have its day.

Whenever someone came along to show me that life could be different than I held it to be, my keen mind could always ferret out the bullshit. Now there isn't one of us whose genius is not mixed with a little bullshit. So I could always find some and let that invalidate any possible value. This was true even of my early experiences with Rolfing. As the work opened up my body, I began to experience new and wonderful energy. At the same time, I became very aware of the specifics of my blocks, my tightness, my distortions. "See, I was right. Life is just a pile of shit."

I began to see that pattern in my own life. I began to see how much it was present in my clients. Rolfing, like anything else, can be used to enhance one's life, or it can be used to prove in a more sophisticated way how fucked up one really is.

The world just is; my body just is. Good and bad arise from my relationship to it. I can create positive or negative value in every event and aspect of my life.

One of the most radical programs that direct our life is the notion that our body is a given that, with the exception of patchwork here and there, changes only in the direction of deterioration.

Here is an exercise: Let these questions float through your awareness for a few days: What limits do I place on my bodily changeability? How changeable is my body? Note what comes up for you when you entertain these questions. Especially note your resistances to them. See, in the light of day, whether your answers are indubitably valid or whether they are based on what "they say."

My goal in the fourth session with Ray was to continue the work of restructuring his pelvis by lengthening his adductor muscles that travel along the inside of the thigh from below the pelvis to just below the knee. As we worked, he sobbed softly. At one point I asked him if he had grown up too fast. He seemed so old to me, so immersed in the games of adult life. "Of course I did. I was sent away when I was in the ninth grade. And I'd never been in a city before. I never related to boys my own age. The girls I made friends with were all older. And we always lived on army bases. I really didn't have much fun." I asked how he felt about his parents' part in all that. He replied very rapidly: "I love them very much. They are wonderful people and have always been wonderful to me. They had nothing at all to do with that. They had to send me away to school." I observed that we can be angry at people with the realization that the anger may have no reasonable justification. "Yeah, I never thought about that," he replied, his eyes lighting up.

His adductor muscles were extremely tight. He found the work difficult but fully cooperated to lengthen the muscles. We parted for another week.

The Adductor Muscles

The tone and structure of the adductor muscles are of major significance in sexual responsiveness. These muscles often pull the pelvis so far out of balance that a great deal of strain is put on the floor of the pelvis, the pubococcygeus muscle, illustrated looking down from above the pelvis. That results in a blockage of sexual feeling and the ability to enjoy full orgasms. The restructuring of the adductors allows the pelvic floor to find a more appropriate position, improving its tone.

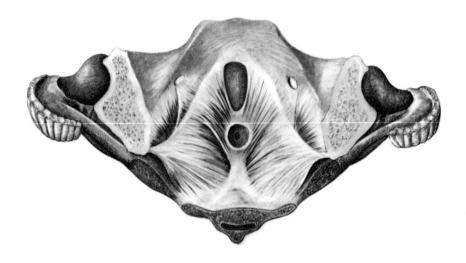

The Pelvic Floor

So much of the uniqueness of your present bodily form goes back to your very earliest days. You may have had a difficult delivery in which your skull was slightly distorted. You notice in your baby pictures that your head is not quite symmetrical and that now your left eye is set slightly lower than the right. Or your hip bone may have been displaced at the pelvis, and you still have that imbalance, but exaggerated by years of dealing with it. Early intrauterine or birth experiences may have put tension in your body that has continued to grow throughout the years, so that your chest, which has always been tight, is tighter now than ever.

Then come the series of accidents or illnesses. When I was about a year old, I fell, hitting my head on the coffee table and blacking out. Mom was terrified. She called next door for Dad. I awoke to their concerned faces. When I was four years old, I had the flu. The doctor came and asked me to put my chin on my chest. I couldn't. I was sent to the hospital for four horrible days and nights, which I have always remembered vividly, to see if I had sleeping sickness. All my life, I have had a stiff neck. I used to experience chronic pain there. Now at forty-two years old, thanks to good old Ida Rolf, I can move my neck more than I ever could, but I still can't touch my chin to my chest.

Many people have had polio when they were young, often undiagnosed. Polio deeply affects the psoas muscle and the integrity of the pelvis and legs. Many persons have had drastic experiences such as being put in iron lungs or incubators, all of which leave profound marks on the connective tissue. Others have had serious falls or been hit by automobiles.

Sally is twenty-six. When she was five years old, she had a serious inflammation of her left hip socket. She was unable to walk for several weeks, and when she did, she favored the hip. Now her body structure is unique. Her pelvis has shifted significantly to her right and twisted back on the right side, her torso has shifted to the left, and her head to the right.

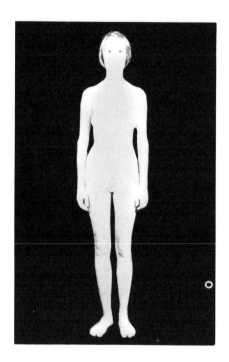 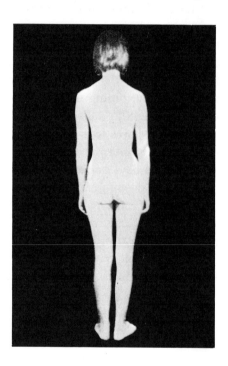

Tom is twenty-eight. When he first came to be Rolfed, I observed that he must have had an accident sometime in his youth because his rib cage looked as if it had been pushed about an inch to his right. He said with great certainty that he had had no accidents. He asked his parents and they confirmed his memory. During his ninth session of Rolfing, I was freeing and separating the distorted ribs on his left side. In the midst of deep sobbing, he recalled that when he was eight years old, he had fallen from a tree onto that side, breaking several ribs; he had been taken to the hospital, and had almost died.

For most of us, the series of events that led to our present physical form are less drastic: falling on one's tailbone several times when skating, spraining an ankle here and there, twisting one's wrist. But the ankle that is slightly distorted at age five produces an arthritic leg forty years later.

I was working on a woman's knee one day. She said she had hurt it in a fall when she was ten years old but didn't think it worth mentioning because it was so insignificant. I explained that what may seem insignificant to her may in fact be important because of such factors as the way our parents reacted. At this, her face became flushed. "Well, in that case, it certainly was insignificant," she said angrily. "My father was never even home to know I had an accident."

Added to the history of our accidents is the environment we lived in: the way the people around us, especially parents, used their bodies. That is the fundamental lesson that produced the structure we have now. Watch a little baby crawling around. You might notice, for example, that the lower

back is often shortened, with the ass way up in the air. There will often be a shortening in the back of the neck due to the way the child must look around and up at his surroundings. Now Mommy and Daddy also have tilted pelves and shortness in the back of their necks. So when the little tyke takes up walking, he retains the short neck and lower back. And what do you know, doesn't little Johnny look just like his dad, swaggering down the street there? It is important to notice that the short neck and back are positions of comfort, appropriate to infantile movement. But Johnny's retention of that pattern in the upright posture no longer flows from inner comfort but from imitation of his parents. As his later history will show, the pattern isn't appropriate for adult movement.

There is also our "womb history." We each spent our early life in a unique way. Johnny's right leg may have been crossed over his left. The lack of space in his mother's body may have prevented his skull from fully expanding and caused it to twist in its relation to the neck. Moreover, his mother's world—her diet, her breathing patterns, her ways of moving, her accidents, her emotional reactions—creates Johnny's environment. Any rotations in the mother's structure or lack of space will be reflected in the structure of the growing embryo.

Adulthood—whether in mind, spirit, emotions, or body—is something to be attained, something to be developed with skill and nourishment over time. Adulthood in the body has to do with balance and length: lengthening the germinal muscles of childhood; balancing the front and back, right and left, top and bottom. It involves allowing the body its full expansion outward and upward.

What I frequently see in older people is children's bodies with wrinkles and aged skin.

One aspect of our self-destructive programming about the body is the illusion that the newborn baby's body is where it's at. We want to be there, obviously can't, so here we are, stuck in misery. Wipe the tears from your eyes and take a good look at the baby's body. Her legs are so crooked they couldn't begin to support her. But even if they could, her body would collapse on those tiny little feet twisted at the ankles. Her cute, smiling, soft head is on top of a very short little neck. The infant is a pink, soft, gooshy blob of infinite possibilities.

Notice another thing about the baby's movement. Although from one standpoint she moves with a grace and spontaneity that is often lacking in her elders, her movements are highly simplified and limited. Compare the way she uses her hands with the way an eight-year-old piano player uses her hands. Or watch a slow replay of a professional tennis match with an eye to the infinite variety of movement in the players' bodies. Or think of the mobility in your pelvis as you dance or make love.

In 1975, Dr. Dick Schultz, chairman of anatomical studies for the Rolf Institute, directed a medical school dissection of the corpse of a two-day-old infant. Already, you could observe some of the major restrictions found in the adult: very tight muscles along the lower back, shortness along the outside of the legs, a buildup of gnarled fascia along the bottom of the pelvis. The two-day-old body showed signs associated with a long and stressful life. The nine intrauterine months assumed the significance Freud saw in the early years of infancy.

There are two functionally different groups of muscles in the body: the outer musculature, with which we are most familiar, including the biceps, pectoralis major, latissimus dorsi, and the glutei; and a system of muscles that lie deeper, closer to the center of the body. This system includes the psoas, the intercostal muscles, the interspinals, the rotators of the pelvis, and the deep muscles of the neck (see illustration). The baby uses the outer musculature almost exclusively. Movement in the deeper muscles has not yet been evoked. It may never fully be evoked unless the child encounters people who themselves experience the full range of body movement. If his father is a craftsman, for example, he may learn all the subtleties available to hand and fingers. If his mother practices yoga, he may learn a way of moving his back that evokes deeper muscular activity.

A common picture of the body that many people report to me is of an outer muscular shell covering inner glandular and organic contents. We are myofascial beings all the way through. Psychological and spiritual depth has a bodily component. A bodily aspect of becoming an adult is learning to use the entire body, evoking movements at all depths of our bodily being.

The outer musculature moves at a faster rate than the inner. It is useful for protection and flight. When it predominates in the life of the body, you have body armor, which protects you from feelings and the perception of others' feelings. The overdevelopment of this layer preempts the activity of the deeper muscles. They become atrophied. Developing an inner life as you grow into adulthood has its bodily component.

I want frequently to call your attention to allowing yourself to simply observe without praise or blame, without saying this is good or bad. Our personal history is part of an ancient history. Mankind is one body, a growing being who experiences fits and starts, reverses and apocalyptic leaps forward. We can say, "Oh, shit, this is my history"—or, "This is my history; let's get on with the show." That your skull is more compressed on

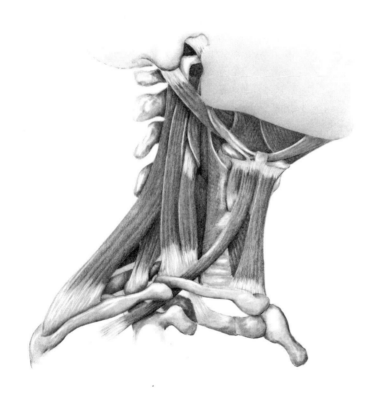

Deep Muscles of the Neck

your right than on your left and that your pelvis is rotated slightly to the left isn't good or bad. It's just the way it is. And if you experience it just the way it is, you'll discover new energy and ease.

I take pictures of my clients at the beginning of the Rolfing process and at regular intervals thereafter. I use them for my own study and to educate the person about her own structure. The experience of being photographed in underwear, standing simply, without posturing, is more painful for many people than the manipulation itself. "Oh, I look so horrible. I hate looking at myself in the mirror. I hate your taking a picture of me like this." At these moments, I appreciate Ida Rolf's teaching me an egoless relation to my own and others' bodies. I relate to bodies as I do to the Grand Canyon, the Mojave Desert, or the seacoast. I experience the ancient quality, the ruggedness, the beauty, of irregular forms that evolved in response to great stress.

I used to complain a lot about the barren high desert terrain around my home outside Santa Fe. In the midst of the complaining, Elissa and I would plant fruit trees, haul in loads of horse manure and grass clippings, replant cholla and chamisa. We now have a beautiful and fertile piece of land. The complaining served only to make things harder, thus proving my original position that life is indeed tough.

What is *bad* is hassling ourselves for doing what we've done with our bodies, or for what we've communicated to our children's bodies. The hassle is of no value. It just drains us of useful energy.

If, as parents, you're serious about serving your kids well, you'd best learn something about the body, and not just first aid and how to spot the first signs of a cold so that you can pop aspirin and antihistamines into their not so receptive mouths. Learn how really to express care for the body, how to massage it, to improve the circulation in a sprained ankle, how to relieve a headache with only your hands. Become clear about the deeper issues: unconscious teaching about the body that you're communicating to your kids, inefficient and even harmful habits of body use, ways to maximize all the body energy available. Perhaps one of the most important lessons for a parent to learn is how to assist a child to relate to pain in a productive way.

The most dramatic experience of my first series of Rolfings was the realization that a central motive force in my life was the avoidance of pain and that the avoidance of pain causes more pain. I lived a very sheltered life, never taking physical risks like climbing high trees or playing contact sports because I was taught how awful it is to get a broken arm or leg. So I never broke a bone in my life, but my body became deadened and stiff over the years, and by my late twenties I was in constant pain.

Freud's genius was to discover the vast effort we employ so as not to experience the pain of a given event. And the unexperienced event literally freezes in our bodies. We keep unconsciously reliving it mechanically again and again. By the time we are adults, we have lost our capacity to respond to what is going on here and now because we're so busy responding to the past.

So, as you let your memory wend its way through the events of your life that formed your present body, realize how the unexperienced aspect of these events has frozen into your body. It's not a big deal to sprain an ankle. But fearing the possibility that I may experience more pain, I put lots of effort into avoidance. I favor the ankle too much, producing a distortion in my hips and spine beyond what the simple sprain would ever have caused. Moreover, the specific fear of hurting the ankle is frozen into the tissue itself to recur automatically in similar situations.

Add parental reactions to your experience of painful events: Johnny falls and experiences a simple pain that doesn't seem at all significant. His terrified mother runs up and scolds him. He begins to learn to make something significant of the twisted ankle.

A favorite instruction that Ida Rolf gives to clients while they are being Rolfed is, "Try to make it hurt more." She knows that if we focus all our awareness on the pain, it lessens.

Your body is your history of your unique path of avoiding pain.

Add to your considerations of your personal history the unique ways in which you've used your body or not used it. You might have started in early elementary school developing an athletic body, playing football and doing calisthenics, eventually taking up weight lifting and boxing. That development is with you now, perhaps buried under extra layers of flesh. You may have danced a lot. Or, like myself, you may have spent many years in a chair or at a desk, reading and writing. Or an early disease may have crippled you, so that you have had to sit in a wheelchair for most of your life.

There is also the emotional history of your life: your relations with your parents, their relationship, how you felt about yourself, your relations with other people.

Rachel is twenty-five. She works at a job she likes, has a loving boyfriend. She is miserable and has no energy. Her shoulders are so wrapped around her ears you'd think she expects to be assaulted from behind at any moment. One day I was loosening the fascia around the pectoralis minor muscle. Tears began to flow. "When I was little, my mom used to scold me all the time. Whenever I heard her footsteps outside in the hall, I did just what I'm doing now, tense up my shoulders around my neck."

Mary is thirty-five. She has a healthy, comfortable body, except for a head that is set unusually far forward of her shoulders. She has a complete set of photos of her childhood and adolescence. Up until twelve, she was very erect and beautiful. Suddenly, her head came forward in the pictures and a look of sadness appeared that is still there twenty-three years later. She cried as we looked at the pictures, saying her father left them that year and they didn't see him again for six years.

Another component in the way you now are bodily is what you learned about the body in a more explicit way: how you should hold yourself, what you should do about your droopy head, your pigeon toes. Steve is thirty years old, a Jewish man from Manhattan, whose early years are reminiscent of Philip Roth's. He held his body very rigidly, with his shoulders and pelvis thrown way back. One day he told me that his mother used to make fun of his genitals bulging in his pants, so he tried to draw them back so that they wouldn't show.

During our early years, we learn all kinds of things about the body: the meaning of standing straight, of relaxing, of strength, of speed, endurance, grace, clumsiness, being handsome or ugly. We also learn shame for the body and lessons about sex that have their effects in the body.

Every single factor that has contributed to your bodily being at this time can be changed, reversed, alleviated—once it is recognized as simply a variable in a personal history and not part of an immutable structure. The tragedy is to view your here-and-now body as the inevitable result of a history that has become concrete in the flesh. There is no concrete in the flesh; it's all moving, breathing, changing tissue, always ready with the least bit of support to rid itself of all the poisons from the past.

4

Beauty and the Beast

Our personal history takes place within the larger ambience of a culture. The various ways we shaped our bodies as we learned movement patterns from our parents are themselves individualized responses to the ideals of movement projected in this culture at this time. Even our bodily response patterns—the ways we reacted to pain, the styles of our reactions—are reflections of popular notions of strength and weakness, beauty and ugliness.

"The social body constrains the way the physical body is perceived. The physical experience of the body, always modified by the social categories through which it is known, sustains a particular view of society. There is a continual exchange of meanings between the two kinds of bodily experience so that each reinforces the categories of the other. As a result of this interaction the body itself is a highly restricted medium of expression. The forms it adopts in movement and repose express social pressures in manifold ways. The care that is given to it, in grooming, feeding and therapy, the theories about what it needs in the way of sleep and exercise, about the stages it should go through, the pains it can stand, its span of life, all the cultural categories in which it is perceived, must correlate closely with the categories in which society is seen in so far as these also draw upon the same culturally processed idea of the body."*

This chapter is a meditation on the relation of the present structure of your body to the male and female images popular in the culture. A major goal of this book is to assist you to experience your body more fully and with greater discrimination, to be able to listen more attentively to the messages it sends about how *it* wants to move or sit or breathe. The theme of this chapter is that popular notions of the attractive body often obscure the inner messages from the body itself. There is often a conflict between wanting to "look good" and wanting to function well.

The first chapter noted that the "real" is for most of us a matter of cultural agreement: what most people say and think is real. The same holds for beauty, which the medieval philosophers recognized as simply another viewpoint on the real. A beautiful body is what popular consensus holds to be beautiful. The consensus varies from age to age and from country to country. The ideal feminine body for the Greek during the Golden Age as projected, say, in the Venus de Milo is different from its Egyptian counterpart, say, Nefertiti. The heavily muscled male bodies of Praxiteles differ from the bodies of the Persian soldiers the Greeks were fighting. The plump, voluptuous nudes of Reubens differ from the equally voluptuous Tantric yoginis carved on Indian temples, and both differ from Hugh Hefner's bunnies. The Western military body seen in the Roman ideal of man around the first century is greatly different from the bodies of Chinese soldiers of the same era.

The bodily ideals of a culture are creative: in their light we shape our bodies either in imitation of them or in rebellion against them. We feel either good or bad about our bodies—ourselves—in relation to those ideals.

Joe has a long history of heavy activity with this body: he was a bronc-

* Mary Douglas, *Natural Symbols* (New York: Pantheon Books, 1970), p. 65.

51

buster in rodeos, a weight lifter, wrestler, gymnast, and lately a karate practitioner. He has invested about thirty years' worth of energy in developing what he once thought was the sexually attractive male body: large chest, back, and shoulder muscles; narrow waist and pelvis; large thigh muscles; and a thick, short neck. When he came for his fourth Rolfing session, he reported that his wife was very upset with the recent changes in his body. She did not like the widening of his pelvis and waistline nor his softening belly. She had been encouraging him to give up the Rolfing even though he was experiencing so much of value from it.

A goal of Rolfing is to create "span," a toned distance between the bottom of the rib cage and the top of the pelvis. For most people, this involves lifting the whole rib cage off the pelvis, coaxing the eleventh and twelfth ribs out from their commonly depressed positions. It also involves stretching and repositioning the quadratus lumborum muscle that spans the distance from the twelfth rib to the top of the pelvis and lengthening the connective tissue of the belly and lower back. The functional results of this work include increased space, with better functioning for the viscera; greater ease in breathing; increased mobility in the pelvis that may improve sexual responsiveness. In the athletic body, the visual change is often a widening of the pelvis and waistline, accompanied by a softening and lengthening of the belly. For the softer, more compressed body, on the other hand, the result is often a longer and narrower waistline.

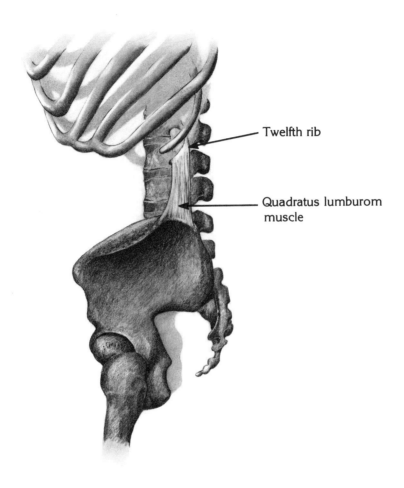

Twelfth rib

Quadratus lumburom
muscle

The Quadratus Lumborum Muscle

Henry, an engineer in his forties, had consciously developed an aggressive body through weight lifting and calisthenics. Most of the muscular development was in the upper part of his trunk; his chest was thrust forward over a tight belly and narrow pelvis, and he had very slim legs. He complained of sexual inadequacy and of being overcome by feelings of rage and hostility. As the Rolfing progressed, he was horrified by the expansion of his pelvis and lower rib cage. He finally decided to inhibit these changes by using old exercise patterns, particularly sit-ups, to halt them. He continued consciously to suck in his belly.

There is a popular misconception about the structure of the belly which involves many people in a vicious circle as they try to deal with an unwanted "pot." The misconception is that a potbelly is always caused by excess fat or by flabbiness in the belly wall. For many of us, however, the potbelly is caused by compression throughout the whole body, usually accompanied by a tilted pelvis. The vicious circle is this: if your pot happens to come not from fat nor lack of tone but from compression and you begin to do exercises to strengthen your belly wall, you are increasing the compression and making it actually more difficult to maintain the slim waist.

In the photographs reproduced on the facing page, you will notice that the man has lost much of his pot in the second photo (taken after a few sessions of Rolfing) by lengthening his body: his rib cage has lifted up off his pelvis, which itself is slightly more horizontal; his head has emerged out of his shoulders. For years, he had tried to lose his pot by doing sit-ups and dieting. He had become extremely discouraged, not only because he never lost his pot, but because he had contracted several abdominal problems, chiefly ulcers. Women who have had several pregnancies often experience a similar problem of trying to deal with a sagging belly by strengthening the rectus abdominis muscle, when the problem is the strain in the deeper muscles, particularly the psoas, and the complex pattern, accentuated by pregnancy, that causes the tilted pelvis. Here also the effective answer is length, not tightening.

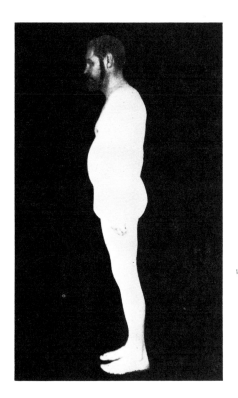 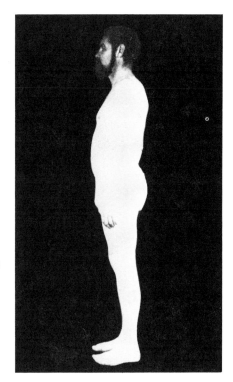

One of the perversities of our cultural teaching is that, of the many varieties of possible structures, only a very few are held up as ideals. Using the categories developed by William Sheldon, the father of body taxonomy, for example, there are eighty-eight body types among Caucasian males. Only about three of these types, which Sheldon calls the extreme mesomorphs, encompass the bodily ideals of our culture: muscular men with large shoulders and slim hips, like the one pictured on the next page. If you are among the eighty-five other types, you spend your life hassling yourself because you can't be an extreme mesomorph. If, for example, you

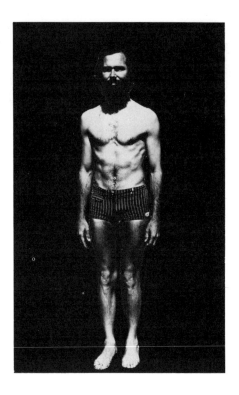

are an extreme ectomorph, with a tall, slender body, narrow shoulders, and narrow hips, you might spend your life lifting weights, doing fifty sit-ups and push-ups a day, ending up at forty with a dropping head and sagging back, discouraged because, damn it, you're still an ectomorph.

The perversity is intensified by the fact that the ideal is the extreme mesomorph during his teens. Sheldon has found (as have most of us) that such bodies tend to thicken in middle age, becoming wider around the waist, putting on an average of fifteen pounds, losing their granitelike contours. So even if you're an extreme mesomorph, you're saddled with the job of maintaining your teen-age figure as you grow older.

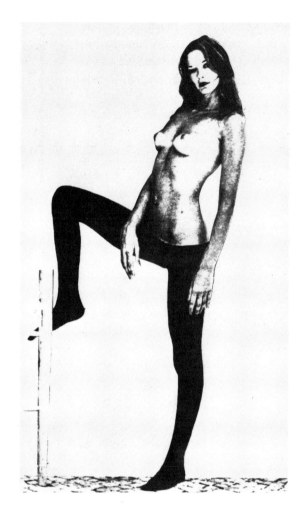 

Women are faced on the one hand with the fashion model imagery and on the other by the sex symbol, which again are models of only a fraction of the kinds of female bodies that actually exist.

Appearance and function are confused. The images of male and female beauty projected in our culture do not, in fact, provide the best functioning for the body. Most of us are confronted with a choice between having a body that looks good in terms of the media images or a body that functions well.

More specifically, these characteristics are common to most of the body images popular in our culture among both men and women:

1. Tight chest muscles compressing the upper ribs and inhibiting the full expansion of lungs and heart.

2. Overextension of the large muscles of the upper back contributing to the compression of the front.

3. Tightening of the connective tissue around the waistline, which inhibits the respiratory system by restricting the diaphragm. It also restricts the functioning of the viscera and the movement of the pelvis.

4. Tightening of the muscles of the buttocks and the outsides of the legs accompanied by an outward rotation of the soft tissue of the legs. The tightening contributes to immobilizing the pelvis. It also contributes to the degeneration of the foot by throwing too much of the weight toward the more delicate outside border of the foot.

5. Distortions in the vertebrae of the neck and in the sacrum, which are critical areas of the nervous system.

Neither the *Vogue* model nor the *Playboy* bunny nor the athletic hero enjoy full breathing. Their pelves are extremely tight. They're at least candidates for sexual, digestive, and respiratory problems. The real message of these images is their perversity: we follow them to become more attractive, but they project the very kinds of body structure that inhibit feeling and responsiveness.

Project yourself into the bodies you view in the media with an eye to function. "If I have that form, what happens to my breathing, my walking, my lovemaking, my defecating? What kind of discomforts might I develop?"

Those questions return us to the notions of programming raised in the previous chapter. Are my life values centered on projecting a pleasing image to the world, or on having an intrinsic sense of well-being? Am I willing to sacrifice a sense of well-being, even sexual well-being, for the sake of appearing attractive, where "attractive" is defined by popular consensus?

My stepson, Michael, a tall, dark, handsome eighteen-year-old, recently came home with proofs of his high school graduation pictures. Several shots captured his tall body and alert, smiling face. But the photographer, Mike said, wasn't pleased with them. In several shots, she had him hunch forward at the shoulders, arching his head and neck forward, with his head twisted to one side. He found those positions very painful, but she thought those *poses* were the best and encouraged him to buy them.

FURNITURE

From the standpoint of maximum ease and efficiency of body functioning, there is very little well-designed furniture. Few chairs allow the pelvis to be in a comfortable position to support the upper body or the head to rest on the shoulders. Furniture reflects the cultural notion that ease is complete passivity. The model of perfect ease is the supine body. So the best chairs

for old Mom and Dad to have are the ones that get them as close as possible to the comforts and drowsiness of bed while still allowing them to look around the room at their guests.

Among the worst culprits, because of their distortion of hundreds of thousands of bodies, are school desks and automobile seats. Both put tremendous stress on the sacrum and throw the head forward, causing frequent headaches and pains in the back.

Appearance and function need not be at odds. The bodies that I now find attractive are generally those that function well. As my own attention has turned toward the better functioning of my body, my aesthetic sense has also changed.

Without moving, check yourself out right now. Observe your breathing, the feeling of support in your pelvis, the feelings in your neck, head, and eyes. Now see if the chair in which you're seated will allow you to be in the position of maximum comfort and ease you know is possible for yourself.

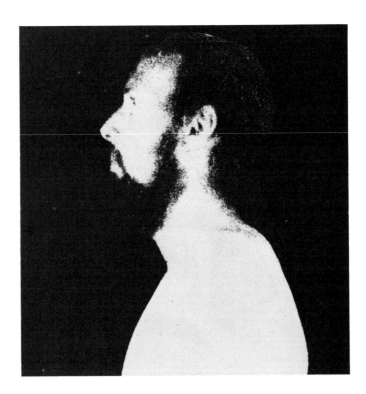

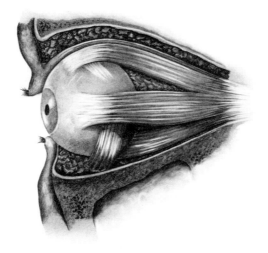

The Musculature of the Eye

Eyes participate in the plasticity of the body. When the head is set comfortably on the neck and shoulders, when the plane of the face is vertical, the muscles of the eye are balanced. If the neck is arched forward with the head tilted back, as in the photograph on the opposite page, the eyes, when looking straight ahead, are actually tilted downward in relation to the skull. That puts imbalance into the muscles of the eye, distorting the shape of the eye and causing problems with vision. With children sitting six hours a day five days a week in a chair that encourages them to cast their heads forward, having to tilt back to peer at a poorly lit blackboard, it's not surprising that many are diagnosed as needing glasses. "Well, hell, it's a lot easier to slap a pair of specs on little Johnny than to redesign all the furniture in school."

THE ANATOMY OF BREATHING

Our culture projects a great amount of confusion about the nature of breathing. Ask yourself, for example, where your diaphragm is. Try to see if you can trace its outline on your body accurately with your fingertip. Do you know where the lungs are? What exactly happens in your body when you take a full breath? With those questions in mind, observe the illustration of the anatomy of breathing, trying to locate it within your own body. The air entering the body through mouth and nostrils travels into the lungs, which are encased in the ribs (which, in case you, like me, hadn't feelingly realized, go all around the body). In the ideal case, each rib is capable of a rotational movement on its own curved axis. So, as the breath enters the lungs, their expansion is accompanied by a venetian-blind-like movement of the ribs upward and outward, all around the body. Notice that the top of the lungs is right at the base of your neck; the lowest border of the lungs is in your lower back.

Now notice the structure of the diaphragm (whose cross section is illustrated from the side). Most of its surface is in the back half of the body. The pumping up and down of the belly that most people call diaphragmatic breathing is the action of the rectus abdominis muscle, which actually restricts full breathing. When the diaphragm is allowed its full expansion, there is a noticeable expansion in the lower sides and back. Now notice the interdigitation of the lower border of the diaphragm (in the front view illustrated) with the quadratus lumborum and psoas muscles. If the diaphragm is allowed to expand in the back, its lengthening movement will be communicated into the pelvis through the quadratus lumborum, and through the pelvis into the legs via the psoas and iliacus muscles.

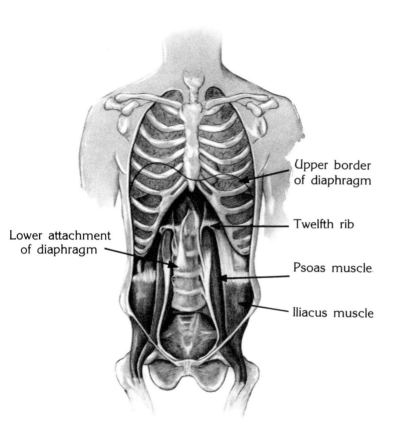

Upper border
of diaphragm

Twelfth rib

Psoas muscle

Iliacus muscle

Lower attachment
of diaphragm

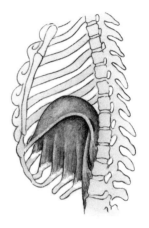

The Anatomy of Breathing

When the entire system is operating, breathing is an incredibly marvelous total body experience. The mothering air enters the nostrils; the torso begins to move up and out, communicating a profound and subtle movement along the whole spine, from the coccyx to the skull; the expansion of the diaphragm lengthens the tissue deep in the belly, communicating movement all through the pelvis, flowing right down the fasciae of the leg into the very sole of the foot. Such a breath can heal pain, relax tension, or introduce needed energy into the body.

The teaching of both chest breathing and belly breathing are distortions based on an emphasis of one part of the system. Those who consciously try to develop chest breathing rightly recognize that the primary receptacle of air is the lungs, located principally in the chest. More room in the chest means more reception of oxygen. The belly breathers recognize that allowing the belly to move and soften allows a person to be more sensitive, more open to emotions, and improves digestion and sexual activity. Both kinds of teaching, besides neglecting the correct insights of the other, tend to forget about the back: the upper back, including the lungs; and the lower back, including the lower sections of the lungs and the back half of the diaphragm interdigitating with the psoas.

The back has become forgotten in our culture. It has been allowed to atrophy, becoming an immovable, wood-like thing "somewhere back there." In most bodies, you will notice that the soft tissue of the upper back has become overextended and is creeping around the sides toward the front. You can often feel long strands of hard atrophied tissue running the entire length of the back. When we breathe, there is little movement in the back. The back sometimes awakens us out of our forgetfulness by expressing its chronic pain, a pain rooted in the forgetfulness itself.

Notice in this drawing the incredible complexity and richness of the back. And that represents only two of the several layers of tissue constituting the back.

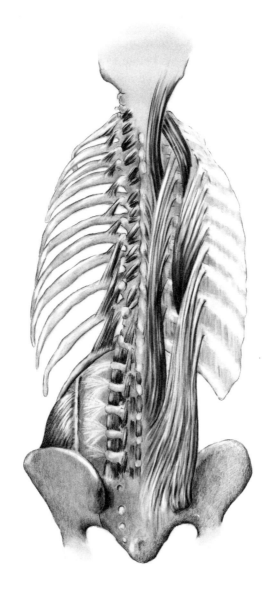

Muscles of the Back

Ray arrived for his fifth session with reports of a painless week. He had studied a lot, played paddleball for the first time in several weeks, and broken up with his girlfriend. As I began to distinguish with my fingers the fascial borders between the rectus abdominis muscle and the pectoralis major, his arms and face went numb and remained so during much of the session. I loosened the fasciae on his arm, and as he experienced what he had experienced as a child when he had broken his left wrist, feeling returned to his arms.

The session proceeded in a fairly straightforward way. My goal was to lengthen the connective tissue of the abdomen: the rectus and its fascial envelopes, and the psoas muscle with its fasciae. I found the same extreme tension at the muscles attached to the anterior superior spine of the pelvis that I found last week in the attachments at the ramus below the pelvis. He stood up looking significantly taller, fuller in his torso, and with his pelvis more horizontal. With great excitement, he asked his mother and his roommate to see the pictures we had taken.

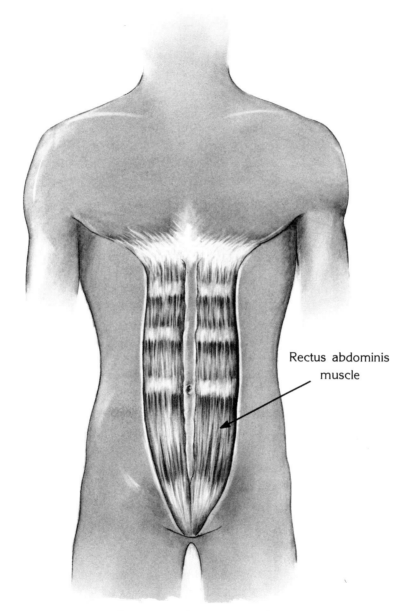

Rectus abdominis
muscle

The Rectus Abdominis Muscle

The psoas muscle is one of the well-guarded secrets of our culture. It is spoken of only in the esoteric circles of orthopedic surgeons, osteopaths, and Rolfers. Artists' anatomy books rarely give a glimpse of it. Body builders ignore it. But this muscle is of great importance in body functioning. It is a major link between movement in the upper and lower halves of the body. Its tightness plays a significant role in lower back pain and sciatica. Its imbalance is a large factor in scoliosis. The abdominal and pelvic nerve plexuses are embedded in its fascia. When it has good tonus and moves freely, it contributes significantly to proper visceral functioning and to full sexual responsiveness.

A forty-year-old salesman came for his first session of Rolfing. He reported a lot of misery: chronic back pain, problems with sex, little energy, and no sensitivity. His body was extremely tight, compressed, and shortened. When I inquired about his physical activities, he said he participated in a directed program of weight lifting and calisthenics at the local gym. He didn't like the program because he found it boring and painful. Although he much preferred just swimming, he hoped the exercises would help him to look better. I explained to him how the exercise program was contributing to the very problems he wanted to get rid of, "So, jump in the pool and enjoy yourself!"

A little boy growing up sees body-building ads on the backs of comic books in which men have tight-assed, tight-bellied, and big-shouldered bodies. The jerks who get sand kicked in their faces while their girls are snatched away have narrow shoulders and pear shapes. His favorite heroes on TV have tight asses, tight bellies, and big shoulders. His dad grew up seeing those same kinds of ideal bodies. The little boy, with his father's praise, finds himself sucking in his belly, lifting up his chest, and working harder at the push-ups dad taught him. As he grows older, he notices that his heroes' women all have tight waists, big breasts, and asses waving in the air. He has fantasies of having such a woman.

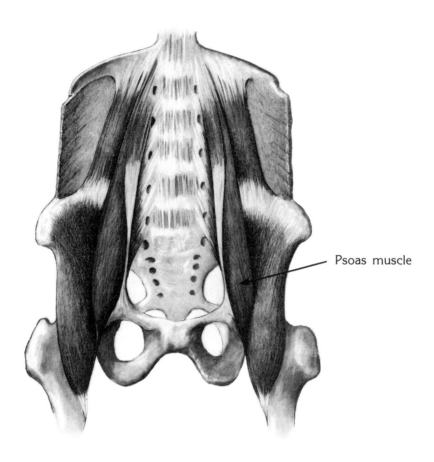

Psoas muscle

The Psoas Muscle

I hated that tight-assed, tight-bellied, big-shouldered image, which I couldn't seem to fit. At the end of my junior year in high school, I went to a workshop called Boys' State, which the American Legion conducts in each state to teach students how government works. When I looked at the picture taken of the inhabitants of our model city in which I lived during the workshop I remember feeling extremely ashamed of my body: I had the narrowest shoulders of anyone in the group.

My relation to the image was to rebel against it, which is just the opposite side of the same destructive coin. I hated sports and I hated what I thought was a weak body. So I withdrew into my own fantasy world, spending hours each day lying on my bed daydreaming. I immersed myself in books and became an intellectual. Cleverly using sickness as my tool to escape the world of the male body, I developed a long history of asthma. I would develop such spasms when I ran that I couldn't possibly play football or basketball with the other kids.

Rebellion doesn't work any better than imitation. I gradually developed a body with a constricted chest, tight shoulders, tight ass, and narrow pelvis. I lost the inner energy, beauty, and sensitivity of my body just as did my contemporaries who took the different route of developing their bodies according to the popular norm.

Our cultural images of the body teach the development of the outer musculature at the expense of the inner. The champion iron-pumpers, the *reductio ad absurdum* of Western body-building programs, give no consideration to the development of the inner muscles of the body. When people think of toning their bodies through exercise, they generally think in terms of developing the outer musculature.

The speed and aggressiveness of Western culture is the outer mirror of that body image. The outer musculature is useful for rapid defense. But its speed and strength are not as useful for more refined sensitivity, for subtler forms of movement, or for making love.

A sixty-five-year-old man once said to me, "I don't understand why I'm in such pain. I hike several miles in the mountains every week. I keep myself in good shape, don't eat too much, don't drink much. I've always taken care of my body." Ray, also, is a model of the healthy American body, but every time he moves, he increases the tension of his body. At twenty, he experiences the body of a sixty-five-year-old.

We are taught through our cultural images that movement takes place by shortening and tensing muscles—by being uptight. As you sit here reading, are you "trying" to see, tensing the muscles of your eyes? Are you working more than necessary to hold up these few ounces? Is your back working to support you? Get up out of your chair being aware of the effort in your body. See if you can gradually reduce this effort until you just rock up and float across the room. Oops! Are you holding your breath?

Our culture—its values, its life-styles, its forms of body activity—is a dramatization of effort. It is born out of an ancient conviction that we have to strive to be something we are not; that life is meant to be a suffering trial for some future bliss; that we are just not good enough the way we are.

One of the uncomfortable experiences people often have during the early stages of Rolfing is to discover all the places where they are always working unnecessarily in their bodies. "My God, I'll just be sitting at my desk writing a letter and suddenly realize that I'm using as much effort as I'd need to dig a ditch!"

Hiking, swimming, yoga, meditating, lovemaking, or defecating can be done through trying and effort, or through opening and lengthening the body. The way in which these activities are done makes all the difference. Every activity done in the first way increases tension and restriction in the body. Activities done in the second way nourish the body, allowing more energy to flow through the system in the form of oxygen, blood, metabolites, nervous currents, and sensory data.

The self-destructive programming of individual childhood appears at the cultural level as well. Are we willing to give up the delight of perceiving the full range of sensory data, the ability to sense the fullness of other persons, the bliss of full orgasms, for the sake of preserving our furniture, our poor diet, the design of our schools, and our desire for more possessions?

I speak most often in this book about the tight body. That's not only because that image is the more popular aesthetically. It's also because my own body is characterized by tightness and rigidity. I know this kind of body from inside my own flesh. There are other kinds of bodies—for example, soft bodies whose principal characteristic is lack of tone. In such bodies, the circulation is poor; there is little support for movement from the myofascial system; the overall energy is low. While my body needs length and discharge of withheld energy, this other type requires the induction of movement into layers of tissue that have been immobile.

AGING

One of the most significant body programs communicated to us through the culture and made concrete in our families regards attitudes toward aging. A general pattern goes something like this: the body grows, matures, and ripens until its prime somewhere in the twenties, then gradually deteriorates until death. The programming can be even more drastic. From my father's way of life, I learned that the body is a painful burden. It's what we men have to endure to earn our way in the world, like Adam after the Fall. From my mother's Catholicism, I learned that the body is a dangerous thing that contained the major attractions to sin that could (and very likely would) lead us to hell. In fact, hell was the eternal fiery torture of this body. (Even though the catechism said the main torture of hell was the mind's realization of being separated from God, that wasn't nearly as real for me as having my flesh burned forever.) So, for me, just being in a body meant steady struggle, burden, and deterioration. Growing old only accentuated those heavy aspects of being in a body waiting for the end.

The cultural norms for beauty are directly related to our attitudes toward aging. Both men and women are affected by the first signs of gray hair, wrinkles, flabbiness, and baldness. "Aging" means losing the outer form of the teen-age mesomorph or the twenty-year-old beauty queen. What concerns so many of us is not deterioration in the inner functioning of our bodies but the change in appearance interpreted as deterioration.

Your own programming about aging may be emerging right now if you're saying to yourself, "But the body is a physical thing, subject to physical laws. Aging is a physically determined process." Do you know what the process is and what are the inexorable laws that govern it? Actuarial tables are not inexorable laws. "Reality" is not what people, even scientists, say it is.

John, a research scientist, is forty-two years old. His legs, which had always been extremely twisted since chilhood, were always giving him trouble: poor circulation, awkwardness, weakness. After a few sessions of Rolfing, the legs had visibly straightened. With tears of joy in his eyes, he exclaimed: "I never could have believed that at forty-two my legs could change their shape!"

For the first thirty-five years of my life, I experienced chronic pain in various parts of my body. I didn't have enough energy to play any sport except golf. At least since I was four years old, I was extremely stiff and tight. I hated athletics and dancing because I felt so awkward and weak. Now, at forty-two, I have more energy than I need; I love dancing and running. I hike distances in the mountains my younger friends find too strenuous. When Elissa, my wife, was thirty-five, she was often bedridden with a slipped disk and had been advised to have a spinal fusion. Nine years later, without the fusion, she is dancing the way she used to when she was twenty, but her body is more flowing, its tone better, and her energy higher.

José is eighty-eight. He lives in a nearby village in a house where he was brought when his family moved there from Barcelona seventy-five years ago. He has always been a rancher and horse trainer, living a vigorous life. He is famous in the area for inviting young ladies to his house to spend the night. He is, they say, a superb lover.

Another model of aging is based on the nature of the myofascial system. At birth, we are an infinite blob of possibilities at the bodily level (as well as every other level). Of the hundreds of thousands of movement patterns that the baby could eventually develop, only a fraction will actually be learned. Some will be developed as the infant learns the basic movements of human life: crawling, walking, and sitting. Others will be developed as specialized skills: how to write with a pencil, how to play ball, to dance, to play the piano, to paint. From this viewpoint, growing old is a continuation of the process of growing up, which itself involves gradual refinement of the body's original undifferentiated capacities for movement. If you're willing to transcend the limits of your programming, you will be capable of more kinds of movement when you are sixty than when you were twenty. Even in the midst of the intensifying of restrictions that have been with us for several decades, we are still able to grow in subtlety and wisdom. Even for a person confined to a wheelchair, there are many possibilities for subtle movement development which are often not suspected.

What emerges from this vision is the possibility of harmonious growth in which the harmony is among intellectual development, bodily refinement, emotional balance, and spiritual wisdom. In this model, neither the blissful infant nor the vibrant eighteen-year-old represent the best of human life, lost forever when one turns thirty. The ideal is the harmony, depth, and wisdom that is possible only after a long life.

"What about the deterioration of physical systems? What about the second law of thermodynamics?" The fact is we don't have the facts. All present physiological theories are derived from observing bodies in cultures that are programmed to age in certain ways. The bodies available for medical research generally are of persons who have not cared about proper diet, exercise, methods of stress reduction, or the relation between psychological programming and body processes. Until we have a large sample of the population that represents a significantly different relation to the body, scientific theories of aging are of as much value as the actuarial tables of life insurance companies. They just indicate the limits of the average person's bodily life in this particular country at this particular time.

There are all around us unique human beings like old José and Ida Rolf who deviate from the average patterns of aging. But like any geniuses, they simply reveal the possibilities that exist in us all.

Again, the issue of pain is significant. In old age, the stakes are higher because the imbalances of the earlier years have become more intense. The pattern is the same: There is an experience of pain (in the back, for example, when getting out of bed); I react in the moment of adopting a posture that alleviates the pain (say, stooping over). But then I carry this posture, which was useful for the moment, into other activities. The stooping makes the body even tighter, so that the pain the next morning is even worse. The thing to realize is that, even at seventy or eighty, the plasticity of the body allows many different responses to pain. There are ways of breathing, sitting, walking, that can greatly ease pain, just as there are many ways to intensify it.

When I was thirty years old, teaching philosophy at Loyola University in Los Angeles, I was asked by the vice-president to take care of the French philosopher Gabriel Marcel, who was visiting for three days. It was a turning point in my life in my relation to aging. As I drove around southern California with this exuberant seventy-six-year-old man enjoying everything he saw, communicating warmly with all the people we met, I realized that he was a different kind of old person than I had ever experienced. He talked with such love and enthusiasm of his wife and children, of all the young students that he was meeting, and of all the wonderful places in the world he had seen. He had flown into Los Angeles on a trans-Arctic flight, the first time he had crossed the pole. He told me how thrilled he had been seeing the immense mountains of Alaska and the vast snowy wastes. We spent several hours just sitting on the edge of the bluff in Playa Del Rey overlooking the entire Los Angeles basin, while he shared his wisdom with me. I realized that all the older people I had experienced until then had seemed deteriorated, saddened, awaiting the end. I had decided that old age was simply that, a sad and inevitable affair. Now, suddenly, I looked forward to old age.

Ida Rolf once gave a lecture on the subject "If Rolfing Is So Powerful, Why Hasn't It Been Discovered Before?" Her answer was in terms of the evolution of culture. The bodily ideal developed by Ida involves maximum ease, speed, softness, responsiveness, and openness to perception. Such bodies are not well adapted to a warlike culture. The rigors demanded of people in past cultures required bodies that were thicker and more armored, just for survival. That is true for both men and women. Although men did the fighting, both men and women by and large lived a physically demanding life: their lives were filled with constant toil. Women had to undergo the rigors of frequent childbirth. Only in this century is a body with maximum ease and flexibility a viable alternative for large numbers of people.

Jim Polidora, who teaches body therapies at the University of California at Davis, writes: "You don't stop playing because you grow old; you grow old because you stop playing."

5

The Body and the Earth

The contributions made to your body structure by the events of your personal history and by the ways you have related to the body images of the culture are exaggerated and often distorted by the ominipresent pull of the earth. Gravity, like air, is so much with us that we don't even notice it except in those rare moments when it dramatically declares its presence or its absence: when falling, or going down the first steep slope of a roller coaster, or walking at the Mystery Spot in Santa Cruz, where the field of gravity is shifted from the vertical; or in the experiences of those few who have traveled in space. For most of us, the events of our history introduce only the slightest imbalances into our bodies. It is moving throughout the decades of our lives with gravity accentuating the patterns of distortion that makes the tale worth telling.

The human form is designed to be vertical in the sense that its systems —circulatory, respiratory, digestive, sexual, lymphatic, nervous—function at their optimum when the body's structure is comfortably balanced in the gravitational field—in contrast to, say, the cat or the deer, whose structures are designed to operate best with their spines in a horizontal plane with the earth. Note that we are talking about structure, not posture. Whether a person is standing, sitting, or lying down, his structure can be such that it is comfortable or uncomfortable in the vertical plane.

But it has not been an easy path for man, a new creature on the face of the earth, to adapt himself to the gravitational field. We are really somewhere in between our primate ancestors and a being whose center of balance is truly aligned with the earth's pull. There have been fits and starts in mankind's struggle to be comfortably vertical. The art of the Old Kingdom in Egypt shows a clearer appreciation of the vertical than was subsequently attained in later periods in Egypt and in the Mediterranean cultures of Greece and Rome. The life-size statues recently discovered in Peking, dating back to the first century A.D., show a remarkable sense of the vertical, as do many Indians now living in the mountains of Mexico. Evolution is not straight-line but cyclical, involving false beginnings and dead ends. But the dynamic is constant: the direction is toward adapting to the environment. And a major environmental factor that is always acting on us is gravity.

The way your body is right now demonstrates the history of your relation to the field of gravity. The body, like any other physical structure, is subject to the laws of physics.

When I was six years old, a neighbor and I were playing in the back yard. As usual, I was playing at being a jerk, so at one point he hurled a baseball bat at me, hitting me in the temple just next to my right eye. Thirty-one years later, when I began to gain an accurate sense of my body, I discovered a radical imbalance between the right and left sides of my skull, reflected primarily in the eyes. The slight imbalance at six had been gradually accentuated over a thirty-year period.

This is a common pattern: one-week-old little Johnny is just beginning to look around his new world. Since he spends most of his waking hours on his belly, he curls his head back to accomplish this feat. He does it a lot during his first year. At the same time, he keeps pretty well curled up in the front of his pelvis, maintaining some of that fetal posture he was comfortable with a few months ago. Also note that in the course of his birth Johnny's head was slightly distorted so that it is twisted ever so slightly to his left. A similar distortion occurs at his hip joint, where the left femur is set into the pelvis at just the slightest angle different from the right. Johnny has already put together his prenatal distortions with his new adjustments to his environment to form a single and unique pattern of body movement. Now, when Johnny begins to walk, he learns from his parents, whose heads are forward of the center of gravity and tilted back, and who have tilted pelves. So Johnny retains the shortness in the back of the neck that he began to develop as he looked around his room and the shortness in the connective tissue around the front of his pelvis. He also leans slightly to the left at his neck and to the right at his hips. Be clear at this point that there is nothing wrong with Johnny. There is no impairment of functioning that is of any concern. He's a healthy, lively baby.

But imagine, with the eye of an architect, Johnny growing into adolescence. Forget he is a flesh and blood organism, bristling with new interests, old hostilities, and many confusions. View him as you would any physical structure. Imagine, for example, what it is like for Johnny to carry his twelve-pound head slightly ahead of the plumb line of gravity. At thirteen, there is, let's say, a two-pound torque that he has to contend with. You can experience what that means if you carry around with you for a while a hardback novel. Just walk with it in your hands, close to your body. Be aware of the slightly increasing strain in your arms, shoulders, and neck. Now imagine that Johnny has to sustain such a weight for several years whenever he isn't lying down. His shoulders and the back of his neck began to develop stress patterns just to hold his head on. The tissue thickens, pliable muscles becoming more like tendons. After ten more years of dealing with the stress of life, the torque vector is now five pounds, since his head has crept just a little further forward. He gets more headaches during college and his eyesight is deteriorating. In another fifteen years, his head has inched forward even more; he enters middle age with cervical arthritis.

Gravity is the constant teacher, always with us giving clues about our being. If we do not learn to dance with her, she will slowly destroy us. But in learning the dance, we derive a new energy that can change our lives.

Note the effects of gravity on your body right now. Without moving, notice how the weight of your body is supported in your pelvis. Note the weight of your head, your shoulders, your chest. See if the weight of your torso is more to one side than another. Does the weight of this book in your hands transmit into your chest or back?

Gravity's high priestess, Ida Rolf, discovered that she could transform the universal field of the earth from foe to friend. She ignored the popular assumption that the passage from birth to death is a steady deterioration of the body due to the downward pull of gravity. She discovered that a body whose large segments are organized about gravity's plumb line can be supported by the earth. Physical life then becomes not a drag but a new source of energy. Aging becomes a gradual appropriation of one's own wealth of experience instead of a process of painful deterioration.

A woman once told me she had been Rolfed by a man whose name I didn't know. She said he was trained in Morocco. I said she definitely wasn't Rolfed; Rolfing is as American as a McDonald's hamburger. Its most esoteric source was learned in the Bronx, where Ida Rolf took yoga classes in her younger days.

Ida Rolf is an eighty-year-old triple Taurus from the Bronx. She looks like a Druid: short, with heavily muscled arms and gnarled hands showing the imprint of the forty years of bodies into which they have plunged. Like most eighty-year-olds who have founded a school of thought with many loving disciples, she's often grumpy and authoritarian. She once gave an interview to Adam Smith, who quoted her as saying that all Rolfers are hacks except her and her son, and there's no money in training people anyhow. She vigorously denied his report, but many of us recognized a familiar if not totally accurate ring in those words.

When she speaks from her center, however, her wisdom is as powerful as any guru's. There are mornings when she arrives at class looking sleepy-eyed, seeming to have prepared nothing. Someone asks a question. We suddenly find ourselves transported into a profound trip linking the fascial network of the body with world history.

In 1920, Ida earned her Ph.D. in biochemistry at Columbia and went to work at the Rockefeller Institute until 1928. Like a true New Yorker, she explored the local healing market, hatha yoga, different forms of body movement, and esoteric philosophy. Her young son had been born with a problem spine that physicians could not help. Seeking elsewhere, she encountered naturopaths, osteopaths, practitioners of radiasthesia, spiritual healers, and yogic physicians. As she began to apply to her family what she was learning, she discovered she could radically alter their bodies. She began to experiment with other bodies and trained her son, Dick, to assist her. Those early years set the pattern for the rest of her life, which she would spend traveling from "pillar to post" (as she often says wearily), living out of suitcases, working on the discomforts of mankind. In an instance typical of those early years, she traveled in a snowstorm all the way from Long Island to work on the stiff back of a countess living at the Waldorf Astoria. She gratefully received five dollars for her two hours' work.

In the early 1960s, Dorothy Nolte, one of the handful of people Ida had trained, met Fritz Perls at a conference in Los Angeles. He had been given a few months to live because of a heart condition. Dorothy gave him a first session of Rolfing, telling him about Ida, whom he immediately invited to Esalen. She packed her bags, leaving her West Side apartment, and overnight became a star of the newly born human potentials movement. She was encouraged to organize her knowledge in a way that could be taught systematically. She started teaching small groups of practitioners—twelve to fifteen a year—until by her eightieth birthday in May, 1976, there were a hundred and fifty practitioners, a staff of well-trained teachers, and a sophisticated program of continuing education. A number of research projects are in progress. Separate groups are developing her ideas in the fields of body movement and in anatomy and physiology.

Like all the geniuses of history, Ida got a very simple insight that unraveled a web of confusion: (1) consider the body as an aggregate of large masses (head, shoulders, trunk, belly, pelvis, legs, and feet) traveling through the field of gravity; (2) realize that the relation between those masses can be changed because of the plasticity of connective tissue; (3) notice that the body functions best at every level (physiologically, mechanically, emotionally, spiritually) when the centers of gravity of the segments are aligned with the plumb line of gravity, balanced front to back and side to side. "So get your hands in that body," she often says. "Stop thinking and get to work." That's all there is to it.

The accompanying illustration, which has become the symbol of Rolfing, is a schematic outline of a child with whom Ida worked. The large segments of his body are enclosed in blocks indicating the relation of these segments to each other within the field of gravity before and after her work.

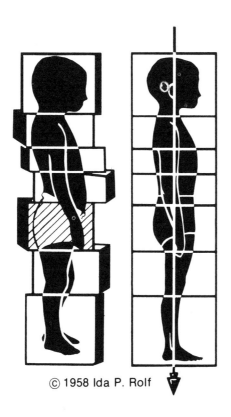

© 1958 Ida P. Rolf

"Biologists have always sought to understand how the form of living things—the shape of a hand, say, or of a leaf—is adapted to their function. We can now begin to see how the shapes even of molecules within cells are related to the mechanics of biological process."* We are also beginning to understand how the human form is related to its functioning.

What constitutes the development of any particular science is the observation of a total system (solar system, nervous system, the molecule) from a viewpoint that produces results. For example, the observation of the solar system within the framework of Newtonian physics produces results. Observation of the same system within an Einsteinian perspective produces more interesting and far-ranging results. Our generation is witnessing the birth of a science about the human body itself as a total system, observed from certain viewpoints—here as a system of relations governed by the laws of physics.

What I learned in my early years is that life is a constant struggle in a hostile universe. Not only am I surrounded by negative forces everywhere, I am also living in a body with an innate tendency to drag me down to an earth that offers nothing but resistance. "By the sweat of your brow, you shall earn your bread." I've invested a tremendous amount of energy in proving that that view of life is correct. When things would begin to clear up or get easy for me, I would always mess it up somehow just to show that I really had to struggle; that I was basically demonic, and that other people, particularly wise people, were out to confuse and tempt me. But I've learned that that's only a picture of life I chose to adopt, causing me to filter my experience in a certain way.

* Carolyn Cohen, "The Protein Switch of Muscle Contraction," *Scientific American,* November 1975, p. 36.

While typing this book, I have been experiencing an old pain that comes from the time when I spent most of my time writing and reading. The pain occurs on the left side of my neck, midway between my shoulders and my head. It feels like a sharp pinching. My tendency has been to open that side, giving it more space by dropping my left shoulder and shifting my head slightly to the right. But the pain continues. As I began typing this chapter, I placed a full-length mirror in front of me and discovered that the compression is on my right side: my right shoulder is habitually lifted above my left, and my head is tilted to the left. As I adjust and balance my shoulders, I feel the remission of the pain.

The basic therapy of Rolfing consists of ten sessions, each lasting about one hour. During each session, the Rolfer uses his fingers, knuckles, and elbows in concert with the subtle movement of the client to achieve loosening and repositioning of the connective tissue of the body. The ten sessions with Ray, described throughout this book, are designed to give you a feel for the pattern of the basic series. The anatomical drawings accompanying the accounts of his first seven sessions give you some notion of the areas worked on in those sessions. For those who have completed the ten sessions, there is advanced work whose goal is to refine the new balance.

The plasticity of the body is what's so. You can hassle yourself about it, saying how miserable and out of line you are. You can become frantically involved in changing your body, introducing more stress in the process. Or you can experience what's so and get on with the show, flowing with the consciousness that comes from experiencing your body just as it is.

This book is not intended to get you to change, but to help you realize you are change.

THE MYSTERY OF UP

The body reflects emotional and spiritual energy in its sense of being up. When we're feeling good about ourselves, cocky, energetic, in command of life, there is a lightness and erectness in our bodies that we lose when we're down, oppressed, feeling bad about ourselves. During adolescence, when Johnny's head went from giving him three to five pounds of trouble, he was depressed a lot of the time, feeling bad about his body, ashamed of sex, unsure of his abilities. He didn't contribute much energy to keeping his head flowing out of his spine onto the top of his shoulders. Gravity, therefore, leaped in to pull him further down. Here is one of the most profound connections between the language of the body ("vertical," "erect") and the languange of the mind and spirit ("high," "light").

The attempt to adapt ourselves to the vertical field of gravity is paradoxical.

At the Santa Clara Pueblo on the Rio Grande near Espanola, New Mexico, is a large three-story adobe building that is reputed to be five-hundred years old. Its walls in some places are at least ten degrees off plumb. The building has stood centuries longer than many seemingly more structurally sound buildings constructed by Spanish and American engineers. Verticality is not its hallmark; thick walls made of mud and heavy beams are its secret. Old José's body is not balanced with gravity; it is heavy and gnarled and distorted. But it has worked well for him. We are asking whether there are other alternatives.

The mysterious "up" is not the same as standing up straight. Standing up straight is something parents and drill sergeants order us to do. It's an instruction to put effort into our bodies, to control things. It suggests militarism, uptightness, lack of spontaneity.

The first lecture I ever gave on Rolfing was at Prescott College in January, 1972. A hostile anthropology professor arose and said, "Philip of Macedon was aware of Ida Rolf's model of the body. It has been passed through the centuries as the model of the warlike soldier." I asked him to demonstrate the model. He sucked in his belly, pulled his shoulders back, thrust his chest forward, and drew his chin back. Everyone in the audience but he was able to see that he was not aligned with the plumb line of gravity in a comfortable way. His neck was short, his head was forward of his shoulders, his pelvis was extremely tilted. There was tension all over his body. But it was an accurate presentation of the military model. That kind of "up" is really down; it pulls the body together, armoring it for protection.

It is often easiest to explain Rolfing to architects. Both Rolfers and architects are trained in what I would call "structural consciousness," an awareness of the abstract patterns of bodies and buildings. Both are concerned with the realization of those structures which maximize the desired functions of their inhabitants.

There are events in the Rolfing process that are like the events in different kinds of psychotherapy, or like what happens when working with an orthopedist or an osteopath. But those are coincidental to the goals of the process, which are to change the structure of the body so that it is in harmony with the earth. The emotional releases and the physical healing that often accompany the process are manifestations of the fact that such problems are often rooted in the body's discomfort in the field of gravity. So, while my goals in working with the person are not to release emotional blocks or cure sciatic pains, that often happens as I move the fasciae into a more appropriate places. You will notice that in the accounts of Ray's Rolfing, I have stated in each session my goals in the work. But other material comes up, some of which is resolved, some of it simply noticed for further development when Ray is ready to deal with those other issues.

Any form of working with the body—Rolfing, patterning, Reichian therapy, bioenergetics, Alexander technique—is of value only when the therapist is using his words, fantasies, fingers, or elbows to teach the flesh the paths of joy and freedom. When I feel in my fingertips nothing but resistance and pain, I know I'm moving in the wrong way; the sense of release and cooperation in the flesh is the clue that my work is going as it should.

The weighty concepts of Ida Rolf have been significantly evolved by her disciple Judith Aston, the creator of structural patterning. A former dancer who was rescued from a back operation by meeting Ida, Judith trained as a Rolfer with an eye toward developing the movement aspects of Ida's teaching. Since 1971, she has been developing an ever more refined method of teaching the body to move in ways that maximize its inner ease and freedom. She has communicated her method to a small group of teachers, including Elissa. While Rolfing involves the rigorous manipulation of soft tissue, patterning, with the use of tactile or verbal cues, teaches people to open and restructure their own bodies from within—by breath, by almost imperceptible shifts of balance, by deep slow movements, and by a highly specific use of consciousness.

Patterning is the midpoint between the basic change of structure that is the aim of Rolfing, and a person's everyday life of walking, running, sitting, digging ditches, dancing, and other forms of human bodily activity. Its sophisticated concepts are also midway between the highly abstract notion of a body balanced in the field of gravity and more specific considerations such as improved furniture design, useful exercise patterns, choreography, and even fashion design.

"Up" is a mystery. I have a close friend who has had years of expert body work and psychological work. He is still down in both body and soul.

Balance and harmony are the goal. There can be several layers of imbalance in the body. Johnny, like me, is imbalanced from right to left. If you look at me straight on, you can notice that my head tilts a little to my right, causing a slight compression on that side of my neck. My pelvis is tipped down toward the left, causing a similar compression deep in my right side near my belly button. These imbalances cause me discomfort and block my energy.

There is often imbalance between the top half and the bottom half of the body, with a highly developed torso, for example, and underdeveloped legs. Often in dancers' bodies, you can observe the reverse: highly developed legs, underdeveloped torso.

There can be imbalance from front to back. I went through most of my life thinking that I was standing solidly on my feet. At one point I discovered that my weight was generally, even when walking, back of the plumb line. When standing, you could push me over with your fingertip. When I was walking, I had to exert more effort than necessary to propel myself forward off my heels.

A more subtle kind of imbalance occurs between levels of the body. At the outer level of rectus abdominis and glutei, for example, you may find the chronic tension that comes from overwork, while at the deeper level of the psoas, there is the atrophy that comes from lack of use. There are, for example, bodies that, though appearing plump and soft, feel like concrete an inch below the surface. There is lack of development in the outer musculature, with a compensatory tightening of the deeper muscles.

There are idiosyncratic kinds of imbalance, such as those arising from birth problems or accidents. A sprained ankle may cause a person to favor the injured side, putting more strain on the other side. Over a period of weeks, the person develops a whole system throughout the body to compensate for the new movement pattern.

Judith Aston has developed the notion of "neutral space." The body harmoniously balanced in the field of gravity is a place from which to move or to which to return. It provides a space from which one can move into effective defense or tender openness. One can utilize the kind of energy necessary to deal with a workday or move into the leisure of being with friends. The dancer and the carpenter can return to a place of greater ease when effort is unnecessary. The actor and the artist have more options and are less predictable.

This neutral space where the body's struggle with gravity is relieved also provides an empty, safe arena in which one can experience what needs to be experienced: past traumata, emotional needs, love, anger, or physical pains that have been suppressed. The neutrality of the space makes Rolfers and patterners comfortable and modest partners with the many therapists, spiritual teachers, and doctors who work specifically with what comes up in this vast arena.

Gravity is our teacher and constant therapist. When we are out of harmony with the earth, she makes it known to us by pains, restrictions in movements, and a host of concrete reminders that we are creatures of the earth. She is relentless, always present, even in sleep, to accentuate the places where we have gone astray.

Aging and death are her most severe lessons. The popular notions of aging, discussed in the previous chapter, are based on a lack of regard for the field of the earth. The deterioration of the body throughout the years is a direct function of its disharmony with the field of gravity. Hardening of the flesh, impairment of the flow of energy throughout the body, the gradual deterioration of joints, and the other signs of aging can all be traced directly to the action of gravity on a body out of harmony with it.

Overcompensation is the dynamic force whereby we allow gravity to deteriorate our bodies. I am committed to maintaining my old body positions. When I sprain my ankle, I want to maintain my comfort as nearly as possible to what I have pictured it in the past, so I adjust my entire body to have the old comfort with the new distortion. My present activity is governed by old pictures. "Hell, I've always typed this way. It's too much trouble to change it at my age."

My goal in working with clients is harmony and balance. I tend to use my right side more than my left. I am willing to sacrifice harmony in my own body "for the sake of getting the job done." But the job cannot be done. I can communicate a more harmonious way of being in a body only insofar as I have experienced it.

As I was about to begin a fourth Rolfing session with a young waitress, she reported having a lot of trouble remembering to stand up straight. It seemed uncomfortable to her. I explained she should be finding ways of deeper inner ease, and available length, not telling herself to stand up straight. I instructed her to work her awareness deep into her body, finding previously unrecognized areas of tightness and releasing them. Let the breath have its day; let it flow according to its own rhythm, lifting the upper body. The discussion suddenly expanded as she realized her perception of "straightness" was like the pattern of her whole life, in which she never learned to respect her own inner rhythms. As a Catholic, she, like me, had been given so many instructions, particularly about sex, that she gave all her attention to either doing the right thing out of guilt or rebelliously not doing the right thing, also with guilt, without ever flowing from her own being and sense of appropriateness.

As more energy is available to the body, outer circumstances and inner crises have less power over one's life. The pure energy of the body feeds into the need for energy at the emotional and spiritual levels.

At the mention of Rolfing, we often envision pain. Many people who have neither witnessed nor experienced the process think of Rolfing as a violent tearing apart of the body. The process is actually a slow, sensitive, and gentle moving of tissue according to the rhythms of the flesh. The pain comes both from the depth of the work and from the conflict within the person. There is in most of us a tension between wanting to be free and the fear of being free. In the flesh, it manifests itself as a conflict between the tissue's moving with my hands and its resisting them. The resistance and the tightening are the major sources of pain. There is also a frequent experience of pain that is the reliving, and more fully experiencing, of a past repressed injury. A person will experience, for example, the exact kind of pain she experienced fifteen years before, when she was hit in the head by a falling board. What many of us discover is that the major source of pain in our lives is failure to experience an event that is painful, whether it be an actual accident or the Rolfer's fingers. We have found that, in either instance, the pain lessens when we allow ourselves to experience the stimulus fully.

A fifty-six-year-old woman whose life has been hard work in the service of others was visiting one evening. I had worked with her three years ago. She kept shifting her position, saying, "When I'm around Don, I always think about sitting up straight." I cringed, realizing the inadequacy of my teaching. The last thing this wonderful woman needed in her life was more worry and effort.

"Up" is the senuous uncoiling of the serpent of feelings lying dormant at the base of the spine, slowly rising with the breath and blood through the center of the body until it flows out the top of the head.

Another cultural myth is that body movement occurs only through the contraction of muscles. The logical corollary of that dogma is that lots of movement, especially the strenuous movement required in sports, means lots of contraction. From that standpoint, body use tends toward deterioration, hardening, and shortening of the soft tissue, because the joints are constantly being pulled together and distorted.

Ida discovered that body movement can also occur by lengthening a muscle. For example, it is possible to learn to move one's leg so that the quadriceps lengthen in concert with the psoas's lengthening and dropping back toward the rear wall of the belly, to rotate the head without shortening the muscles of the neck, to lift the forearm without shortening the biceps.

I said to Ida one day, "How in the hell can you raise your forearm without shortening your biceps?" "Watch," she retorted. She lay a man down on a table, instructing him to move his elbow straight in and out from his side. We all observed that the muscles did indeed shorten. She began to work on the fasciae of his arm and shoulder. Ten minutes later, when he repeated the original movement, there was no contraction. The elbow was moving by the lengthening of tissues—in both flexors and extensors—in the upper arm.

The actual explanation of this kind of movement is still unclear. But there seem to be three states of muscular activity: (1) a state of balance, tone, or rest; (2) a state of contraction; and (3) a state in which the muscle lengthens and falls back toward the center of the body—e.g., the biceps lengthens and falls back toward the humerus to raise the forearm. The latter kind of movement is not easy to come by. It begins to happen in the later sessions of Rolfing, and with structural patterning, but it takes a good amount of time, awareness, and change of mind to build that kind of movement into one's habitual uses of the body.

The consequences of the shift to the third kind of movement are radical. Imagine how many times a day you stand up and sit down, how many hours you spend walking here and there. Every single time you engage in those activities you have shortened your body and consumed energy in the shortening. You have been contributing to the deterioration of your body moving in the earth's field. Now imagine a shift where all this movement involves an initial lengthening of connective tissue. Each time you move, you are increasing the ease in your body, enhancing the flow of energy. Movement, rather than perfect passivity, becomes the nourishing source of the body.

The shift in awareness is essential for my work with Ray. He uses his body constantly in strenuous ways—running, swimming, playing various sports. He is constantly and consciously tightening his body. What life in his body has meant for Ray is effort.

This kinesiological principle is true: In a balanced body, when flexors flex, extensors extend. What is changed is the notion that flexion means contraction exclusively.

Ray's report of what happened in the week between his fifth and sixth sessions was, "Woe, agony, and misery." Monday had been his best day in three months. But that evening, he awoke with muscle spasms the whole length of his back on the right side. The next day he urinated eleven liters. I asked how he knew. He replied he had been curious, so he measured it. He went to a doctor, who could find nothing wrong.

I worked primarily on the back of his pelvis, restructuring the fascial envelopes of the gluteal muscles, the rotators, and the hamstrings. I loosened the tissue around the sacroiliac joint to establish movement in the sacrum. During and after the session, he reported experiencing only pain.

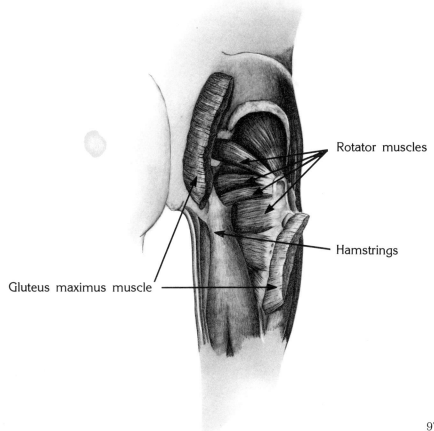

Rotator muscles

Hamstrings

Gluteus maximus muscle

When we finished, I said I had little sense of his inner life: his deepest values, his dreams, the images he lives by—his imaginative side. He looked puzzled, replying that his goals were getting good grades so that he could get into graduate school to get a Ph.D., and that he never dreamed. I asked him why he wanted the Ph.D. He had never thought about that. I asked him to consider those questions during the week, allowing for the possibility that his constantly recurring physical pain may be telling him that what he is getting in life he doesn't want, and that there is something he wants in life that he isn't getting.

"Up" and "length" represent new goals for a more harmonious relation to the earth, to ourselves, and to one another.

There is a wonderful fairy story by George MacDonald, illustrated by Maurice Sendak, called "The Light Princess." It tells of an infant princess whose wicked aunt, accidentally uninvited to the princess's christening, retaliates by stealing her gravity. The princess spends her childhood years in sorrow, alone and unable to relate to other humans, floating at the end of a tether. It is only when, at the end, with the help of a prince she regains her gravity that she experiences love.

6

The Body and One's Own Artistry

The course of your personal history, the cultural ideals you learned, and your unique pattern of relating to the field of gravity are but pigments on the palette that you have put together to create the form sitting within your skin. This chapter, a meditation on your creative role in the process of forming your structure, tests the limits of responsibility you allow yourself to take for your body. The previous chapters have invited you to consider many of the factors that have contributed to your present form, this chapter asks for a shift of viewpoint to entertain the notion that you created this structure.

George is the forty-five-year-old son of wealthy parents. As a child, he had a nurse; rarely saw his parents, who were totally immersed in their social world; was sent to the best schools; and graduated from Yale. He learned many sports and had damaged his body in various places around the globe. He had been married three times and had spent years in psychotherapy. He was handsome, robust, athletic, witty, and very intelligent.

As he told me his story before we began his first Rolfing session, I found myself becoming very uncomfortable. I felt ill at ease about the prospect of working with him. I noticed a great disparity between his obvious power and the self-pitying weakness in his narrative. He spelled out in great detail how his nurse, parents, teachers, coaches, and wives had conspired to make his life continually more miserable. Years of psychotherapy had been of no use. With a sigh and a shrug of his shoulders at the end of the history, he added, "So I thought I'd try this."

I told him about my discomfort, saying I thought it came from my feeling that he would use me and the Rolfing, as he had seemed to use everyone else in his life, to prove how completely hopeless he was. Unless we could work that out together, I knew our work would be of no value. I asked him to try out this thought during the week: "I am a creative bastard." His eyes lit up to reveal a different energy level that was more consonant with his outward appearance.

When he returned the following week, he said that he had gotten in touch with his desire to prevent the Rolfing from doing him any good. He had always hated his domineering father, who had shown him little love and was always filled with his own importance. George had learned as a little kid that he could maintain some sense of personal integrity and power by doing things that would embarrass his father, making him look stupid and incompetent in handling George. In those early years, George had decided that that was the most effective way to stay in touch with his inner worth: to show those who were in positions of helping him or supposedly superior to him that they were in fact helpless and incompetent.

From that point on, our relationship was wonderful. He worked with my hands to soften and lengthen the flesh, revealing decades of old rage. He gradually came to recognize how clever he had been in handling his insane childhood environment, and that his present environment required still another kind of genius. He now manifests to people his real power and warmth.

Victimhood or creation—these represent two radically different views of the same life. Our lives are like a Bosch tableau. You can look at your picture on the tableau and say, "Poor me, things were so hard; there was nothing else I could do." Or you can congratulate yourself for having created such a unique piece of art and get on with the ever-changing show.

There is a theory of knowledge implicit throughout this book that here needs to be made explicit so as to forestall obstacles that might easily prevent you from benefiting from the meditations presented in this chapter. In this theory, ideas are not *pictures of things out there;* they are expressions of relationships among various events in the world.

They are not *pictures*. Photographs, memories, dreams, and fantasies are pictures. They are more or less clear or sharp, faded or dim. Strictly speaking, they are neither true nor false. When we confuse ideas with pictures, as did the eighteenth-century empiricists, we eventually become skeptics and often anti-intellectuals. Immanuel Kant clearly showed that a picture in the mind does not have any clear-cut and traceable relationship with whatever produced it, so the correspondence between the picture and its source, which some understand as truth, cannot be had. Moreover, the living, palpable reality is of more value than some watered down, vague picture, "so to hell with ideas; let's get back to reality."

Ideas are not pictures of *things out there*. $E = mc^2$, Jungian psychology, Gresham's law, liberalism, and Marxism are ideas. But they are not pictures of things out in the world. They express relationships among things, people, events, nations, dreams, emotions—some outside our lives, others inside. They are *true* insofar as they enable one to sift through the mass of chaotic raw experience to achieve certain goals. The Jungian notion of the person, for example, is true or false, not as a picture of your mother is accurate or inaccurate, but as it enables you to sort through the chaos of human feelings and emotions to achieve some integrity and peace. They are true insofar as they have valuable results.

This book presents certain ideas. The central idea might be expressed thus: Body structure is a function of at least four variables: the events of personal history, cultural forms, the body's relation to the gravitational field, and one's intentions. That idea, and others in this book, are to be evaluated in terms of their value for you. Do they clarify your experience and assist you in attaining what you want in life?

With regard to the issue of the body as a function of your intention, you can, like me, raise so many theoretical issues that you'll never get down to the business of really asking yourself the relevant question. You can say, "There's no way of knowing that I created every aspect of my life," "The Vietnamese and the blacks are not responsible for the quality of their lives," "A child is a helpless pawn in the hands of powerful parents," and so on. That is to miss the point, which is to allow yourself to indulge in the meditation and see what comes up. See if there is value in the consideration.

Consider your body in terms of what you're now doing with it, in this period of your life. The form of your body will correspond to your chosen directions. If you are a dancer, you might have a long, slender waist, lifted chest, tight ass, and highly developed thighs. If you're a tennis player, a golfer, or a guitar player, you might find your right shoulder has developed much differently than your left. If you are a middle-aged office worker who has chosen not to get much exercise, you'll probably find yourself sagging in the middle, with your flesh losing its old tone, and a little shorter. A nurse might find chronic pain in her calves and the soles of her feet. A scholar may find herself hunched over with head way forward. A cowboy will have the classic bowlegs with a tight lower back and stooped shoulders.

Meditate on this fundamental question: What have been my goals in life?

If you stay with it, several answers will come up. We each have several goals and they all have some effect on our body structure.

There are the more immediate, conscious goals: I have chosen to be a Rolfer. Over a number of years, my Rolfing has resulted in developing a very different body than I had when I was a scholar. I am more muscular. My constant work with the "Rolf line" has given me more physical stamina.

I now have the wide shoulders I wanted when I was a teen-ager at Boys' State. I have also chosen to run regularly, to dance, and to follow a healthy regimen of food and drink.

There are the deeper layers of goals. During the first thirty-three years of my life, my intention was to live outside my body. I lived in a fantasy world of daydreams, books, philosophy, movies. I was celibate. That intention formed a body that was dense, insensitive, and extremely armored in the pelvis. My intention during the last decade has been to experience my body, to confront the pain in it, to learn to use it. That intention has produced a different body structure.

Still deeper. Early on in life I decided to get care and attention by playing weak and sick. My parents always responded favorably to my act. I was able to get out of doing a lot of unpleasant things that way, such as mowing the lawn (I would always get an immediate attack of asthma if I started to cut the grass). Girls liked that number. And throughout most of my life, I found it a successful way to get people to support me. I have learned the uselessness of that intention. My intention now is to acknowledge my own power and to be with people as I am, not trying to manipulate them by playing "little boy" games. These intentions have created my body: I made my body into a sickly thing, particularly by compressing my chest. My pattern of playing sick was centered there: twenty years of intense asthma, frequent flu and colds.

Another layer: my body is very rigid. There is not a great deal of movement in my spine, my sacrum, and my skull. I'm not clear on my intention to create that rigidity, which is probably one ironical reason behind my writing this book on the radical plasticity of the body. What I know is that it has to do with my way of dealing with fear. Since I was a little kid, I decided the world and the world-to-come were filled with dangers against which I had constantly to be on guard. I created a guardlike body that to me seemed useful in this horrifying world.

Still another layer: I intended to relate to the world as a dependent infant and for years I retained the body of infancy: forward head and neck, the mouth tilted up to receive milk from Mother's breast, pelvis tilted back so as not to release the overwhelming power of sex.

Your present body reflects your present life-style. Your life-style reflects your intentions, your life goals, your values.

Sam cut two fingers off his left hand a year before being Rolfed. His whole left side was shortened. He felt miserable about himself even though he had a handsome and healthy body. During his seventh session, while I was working on his head, he began to experience the whole history of his life with his father. His father had slapped Sam a lot when he was very little, especially whenever he would cry. Sam felt his father didn't love him at all. Suddenly, every single detail surrounding his accident appeared to him. He saw himself deliberately sticking his hand into the power saw with his father sitting nearby. Sam experienced his father demonstrating love and concern for him for the first time in his life. His realization that he had purposely maimed himself, and that he had done it to test his father's love, brought intense agony. He sobbed for hours. But the other side of the agony was realization and freedom. The self-inflicted Zen-like blow had now awakened him to what life is about. He was becoming freed of an endless cycle that people pass on of being unable to accept and express love. It was clear that his life would begin to be filled with love.

Sam's agony reveals the central reason for choosing to see ourselves as victims instead of as creators. It's painful to take responsibility for creating the insane movie that is our life. We invest incredible energy to protect ourselves from the pain. But on the other side of the pain is love and freedom.

This chapter is not about "mind over matter." "Mind over matter" has the connotation that things are wrong in my life because my thinking is wrong, because I have negative thoughts. If I clear up my thinking, my life and my body will also clear up. It is an attitude that thinks of the material world as unreal or at least insignificant. Many people who espouse this philosophy shun forms of body therapies and even psychotherapies because they believe that indulgence in such therapies perpetuates the illusion that the physical body and the emotions are real, when in fact they are creations of mind.

Speaking in the language of "intention" is meant to bridge the gap between mind and matter. Intentions are always embodied; they are always a unity of mental attitudes and fleshly activity. The intention to get well, for example, includes not only the handling of negative thoughts but also the implementation of those means that occur to one as necessary to renew the flesh—changes in diet or exercise, for example. Both negative and positive "thoughts" have their bodily manifestations. The thought and the body pattern are not two separate interacting *things* but two aspects of a single pattern of behavior.

We have all made certain decisions in life about pain. For me, the avoidance of pain was a principal motive in my life. My childhood was very restricted because I simply did not want to experience the pain of falling, of cuts, of broken bones. Through the years, the avoidance of pain became both a physical and an emotional wall around my being. I constructed a world to avoid pain. The wall became so thick that I needed heavy artillery (LSD, Rolfing, est) to crash through it.

The different styles that people have chosen to deal with pain are palpable in my work. Some immediately tighten their entire body when I begin to touch them, anticipating intense pain. Some slowly let go and relax, beginning to work with my hands. Some hold on so that I am unable to work with them. Others invariably tense themselves in specific parts of their body: the neck, lower back, between the eyes. Still others relax and accept pain at one level of their body but cannot allow work on another level.

When George was three, his nurse was walking him and his younger brother through the Boston Common. George stuck his little foot in the wheel of the pram and the nurse kept on moving, mangling the foot. Forty-two years later, he still shows the distortion of this ankle throughout his body. I said she must not have liked him. "Oh, no," he said, with sadness and resignation, "she was just trying to teach me a lesson, that I couldn't get away with things like that."

I was working on his side one day and he had a sudden vision of a home on a lake where he and his brother had spent a summer when he was five years old. I asked him what happened then. "Oh, nothing. It was a very pleasant and uneventful summer. The only thing was that my father threw me off the dock into the lake when I didn't yet know how to swim. He stood there and laughed at me. I was terrified."

Conceiving of oneself as a victim causes one to feel anger, hostility, resentment, and uptightness leading to confusion. "It's their fault: my parents, my wife, the government, world history." It is not a place from which one can be of service to the world with clarity and effectiveness.

Nor is there any blame. The worlds of George and Sam, which are our own worlds, are absolutely crazy. They are peopled by generations who have not known how truly to love or to obtain what they deeply want in life. War, hostility, greed, and deception are the hallmarks of this world. Armoring ourselves against this world, pretending it doesn't exist, cutting out a large segment of sensory input from it, are actually creative responses, not to be ashamed of.

But there are alternatives.

The child is hurt. He does not want to experience the pain, so he constructs a physical and emotional system to block the experiencing of the event causing the pain. But the protective system hardens the tissue and mechanizes the emotional response. Many painful incidents handled in this way produce an adult who is rigid, mechanical, and totally predictable.

Joan is twenty-five. She has participated in Gestalt therapy, Rolfing, and Arica training. She follows a rigorous program of exercise and diet.

When she was fifteen, her father died of a heart attack. Joan is afraid of dying of a heart attack. One intention behind Joan's decision to mold her body in the ways taught by various therapies is to avoid death by heart attack. Like many survival intentions, it works against itself. Instead of getting the full value from the various disciplines, she is continually building tension into the various teachings she encounters, so that her body remains basically tight and closed, making it a candidate for heart problems.

When I was an infant, I started playing games to buy love from my parents. I chose to play those games. I chose to get their love, warmth, and physical support by putting on all sorts of psychological costumes. They didn't blackmail me, saying, "Now, you act like a silly clown, little Don, or we won't feed you." Even if they had blackmailed me, I could still have made a choice between death and renouncing my inner being, or I could have remembered that I was playing a game, so as to give it up when I would be old enough to care for myself.

There is a type of person who comes to be Rolfed, usually sent by his doctor or therapist, who seems to be saying to me, "Well, here I am. I'm so terribly fucked up I know there's nothing you can do to help me. I've been to a lot of experts and they haven't been able to do anything."

Our decisions about sexuality have a great impact on the form of our bodies.

The teen-age girl is freaked out by breasts emerging into the world beyond her accustomed boundaries. So she draws in her chest. She's also as tall as, or even taller than, many of the boys in her class, so she tries to make herself shorter by drooping. When I was that age, I was ashamed of not having a bigger body. My particular response was to withdraw from the world of big male bodies: sports, gym, and an active social life.

If you're a man who is unsure about your potency and attractiveness, you may choose to undertake a body-building program to increase your energy, slim your hips, and give your flesh better tone; or you may decide to junk the whole thing, as I did, and become a celibate.

There are as many body styles as there are forms of sexual preference. For example, if you choose to be attractive to men, you will probably shape yourself slightly differently than if you choose to be attractive to women; and within the broad division of homosexual and heterosexual, there remain all kinds of ritual nuances in our culture, all made possible by the radical malleability of the body.

If you intend to be sexually unattractive, you will also shape yourself accordingly, perhaps making yourself too fat or too lean, or making yourself insensitive by armoring your flesh with tension.

Again no praise or blame. We don't say an El Greco is better than a portrait by a local artist because El Greco's bodies are more pleasing, but because of the skill and imagination embodied in his painting. Each of us represents an incredibly skillful imaginative response to a lifetime of data.

Take Johnny. When he was around five, he decided not to let all the hostile information coming from his parents' fighting fully enter his being. He began to shut off his chest and belly, hiding in his room. He decided to respond to his fear of his father by imitating him, by creating the body of a young athlete and being involved in sports. He also found he could get a lot of attention and warmth by acting confused and helpless around his mother. So he began playing that game. He even exercised his creative imagination in relation to the field of gravity. When he fell off his bicycle, with his mom standing expectantly at the kitchen window, he made the most of the opportunity by looking terribly damaged. He limped badly, compressing his body in the area of the injury. When he got into high school, he didn't want to relate intimately with girls because he found them as threatening as his mom was to his dad, so he made himself armored and insensitive to avoid being attracted to them. Now, when he feels the soft warmth of sexual feeling welling up inside, he shuts it off. His pelvis becomes tighter and less mobile.

For most of us, it is not the objective injuries that cause the major and long-lasting distortions in the body, but the way in which we choose to relate to injuries. The average kinds of accidents—sprains, broken arms and legs, pulled ligaments—would not have the overall effects they generally do if we related to them with more clarity. That is true even in drastic incidents, such as car accidents in which major permanent damage has been done to the body. During Rolfing, such persons usually find that they have exaggerated the results of their accidents, developing new styles of movement that they enjoy. For example, I once worked with a man who limped severely and leaned on a cane. After a very little amount of work, he discovered he could walk lightly and easily without the cane. He was loathe, however, to give up his old style, which he was very fond of.

Ray came in for his seventh session saying, "You sure did me in last week. That place in my back where you worked really hurt." I asked him what else had happened. "I was able to play paddleball and run every day without pain."

My goal in this session was to lengthen his neck so that his head could sit more comfortably on top of his lower body, and to get more movement in the bones of the skull. As I began working on the attachments of his neck muscles to the back of his skull, tears began to flow. It turned out that what he originally had reported to me as being kicked in the face by a horse was much more serious than I had understood. In addition to breaking his nose, which had actually been totally smashed, he had also had all the bones of his face broken. Everything had been rebuilt. His upper teeth were a bridge inserted into the rebuilt maxillary bones with wooden pegs. He was terrified of playing sports in which there was a danger of a ball hitting him in the upper bridge, because it was fragile and had been knocked loose before, causing a lot of pain and hemorrhaging. As I continued to work, he remembered the accident in every detail. The most painful memory was of seeing his bloody face in the mirror before he was taken to the hospital.

I commented on what fine work had been done for him by his doctors. You would never guess from looking at him that he'd had such a terrible accident. Everything had been so skillfully rebuilt. His eyes lit up, "Why, I had thirty doctors, the very best." As he described to me their work, it turned out to be three doctors.

At the end of the session, he reported feeling a great deal of relief, along with a lightness in his body.

The freeing of the rest of the body that occurs during the first six sessions of Rolfing makes possible the radical alterations of the head and neck that are the goals of the seventh session. In Chapter 2, I called your attention to the mobility of the bones of the skull. There is also a complex system of connective tissue encasing the skull. The fascial covering of the cranium travels down the temple inside the jaw, as illustrated on the facing page, to become the pterygoid fascia attaching to the sphenoid bone pictured on the cover of this book. This fascia continues down inside the jaw, finally bifurcating into the deep and superficial fascial layers of the neck, which continue down into the trunk. The structure of the fascia is such that the many tiny muscles inside the mouth as well as those in the face continually exert pulls on the vertebrae of the neck. Their imbalance also puts an imbalanced strain on the sphenoid bone, transmitting distortion throughout the whole skull. Ida discovered, under the inspiration of the cranial osteopaths, that disorders of the neck and imbalances in the skull are often a function of imbalances of the connective tissue inside the mouth. Those imbalances often have an intense emotional component. The masseter and buccinator muscles may be tight from years of clenching in anger or withholding tears. The tissue inside the nasal cavity may be compressed, along with the more extrinsic compression of the furrowed brow, sometimes a manifestation of

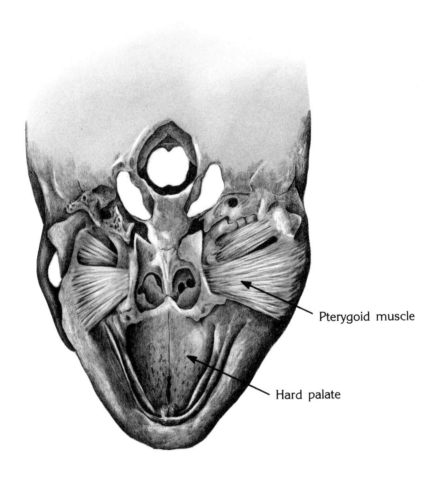

Pterygoid muscle

Hard palate

The Roof of the Mouth and the Skull (from below)

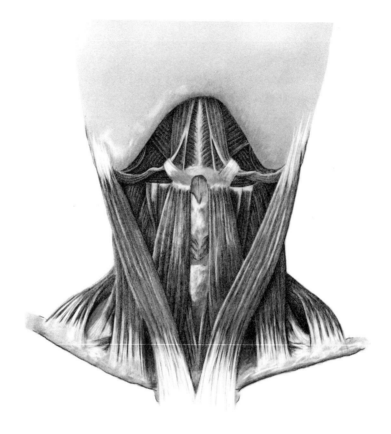

The Neck and the Floor of the Mouth (from below, front)

chronic worry. There are the patterns of tension involving the eyes, the tongue, and the teeth. The refreshing experience of the work on the skull is the realization that it is indeed a part of the body, just like the rib cage or the pelvis or the spine. It's not some Pandora's box filled with dangerous monsters.

I was about to begin a therapy session whose goal was to get out my anger at my grandfather by using sound and beating a large pillow. With my eyes closed, I started by bringing my fists with all my force into the pillow, but my right fist missed, crashing with all my might into a concrete floor. The therapist was disturbed, realizing the value of my right hand and its probable damage. She wanted me to stop and put the hand in cold water. But the rage against my grandfather came pouring out, rage at my buying his approach to the world in terms of weakness. I screamed and beat the pillow for over an hour. I experienced no soreness in my hand then or later.

Try this experiment: When you're standing around at a social gathering, for five minutes put aside your drink and cigarette or whatever you're holding. Just stand squarely on your two feet, with your arms hanging relaxed at your sides. Don't gesture with either your hands or your face. Just be there physically. Observe what comes up—fear, discomfort, panic, whatever.

Our posturing is constant. We can rarely just be with one another in our bodies. We each have developed a bodily act, just as we don certain styles of clothing, to communicate that we like to think of ourselves in certain ways: the thoughtful-looking, pipe-smoking college professor; the cool twenty-year-old rugged mountain man; the liberated woman; the agonized political radical; the reputable businessman and his total wife. When we drop the act, as in the exercise described above, a different reality and different experiences emerge.

Dropping the act is what makes meditation such a powerful experience. One is just sitting there, doing nothing, saying nothing. Just being with oneself.

It is useful to become clear about the origins of your actual choice of playing the victim game: the events of childhood when you adopted your world view. Perhaps things were just too much of a hassle for you to remain in contact with your deepest being, with yourself as source of your experience of the world, so you, like me, copped out, went to sleep for a few decades. Perhaps there was an event—your birth, an accident, a period of parental abandonment—that was so intensely painful that you decided to shut it off and forget who you were.

The important thing is to realize that you, here and now in your body, are the result of your unique putting together of all the elements in your life: your body is the result. If you realize that, you'll also realize that it's all changeable. You can clarify for yourself your intentions. As you do, you may junk some of them, revise the importance of others. This is not a clear-headed, rational process, but the result of a long period of being aware, reversing the flight from experience. It involves fear, terror, pain, and the joy of discovery.

7

The Body and the Body Politic

Unity is a matter of viewpoint. The solid, unshakable notion that I am me, that my body is an independent entity, is no more true or false than to say the earth is an independent entity, or the circulatory system of the body is an independent entity. I am, in fact, a component in larger systems, separated from which I would not survive. On the other hand, the larger systems themselves get their character from the interaction of their components of which I am one.

Chapters 3, 4, and 5 were reflections on the effects of total systems (family, society, and the earth) on body structure. Chapter 6 reversed the viewpoint and began to look at the larger systems as affected by us. This chapter continues the reversal, asking you to look at the ways in which your experience of yourself influences the ways in which you relate to larger systems within your world.

A thirty-year-old musician in the early stages of Rolfing came one day reporting that she was very upset. "I can't relate to people the way I used to. The quality of my relationship with old friends just doesn't satisfy me anymore." During the weeks that we continued dissolving her old body patterns, she reported increasing loneliness. As we neared the end of our work and her body was reaching a new level of balance and harmony, her sadness began to turn to joy. She reported discovering new and more satisfying levels of intimacy with a very small number of people. She felt less needy and more self-sufficient.

"One of the ways you can recognize people who don't know who they are is if they think that when you realize yourself it cuts you off from other people. Somebody who thinks that self-realization is the road to political irresponsibility has demonstrated an absence of an experience of the self."*

My body is the fundamental matrix within which I experience the world. On the basis of my experience, I participate with others in creating the larger structures of the world: social, economic, political, artistic. When the structure of my body changes, my experience changes, thus changing my relationship to the other structures.

In the twilight of the political movements of the 1960s, two of their most articulate spokesmen, Herbert Marcuse and Norman O. Brown, engaged in a debate whose resolution is still important. Both Brown and Marcuse had been prophets of the counterculture with their syntheses of Marx, Freud, and Wilhelm Reich, arguing for a return to the body and its eroticism. They both agreed that the repressive structures of capitalist society were mirrored in the repression of the human body. A return to the body was a revolutionary act. Brown's path of revolution was further down into the body to the body of mankind. It was a path of destroying the body ego, the consciousness of being an individual walled off from the universe. Marcuse took an outward path supporting those groups who were interested in destroying the repressive sociopolitical structures themselves. Marcuse

* Werner Erhard, speech to est graduates, San Francisco, August 15, 1975.

argued that Brown's body mysticism is irresponsible and a more sophisticated form of the sublimation that Brown ruthlessly exposed in *Life against Death.* When millions of people are starving, the entire earth is being polluted, and nuclear holocaust is a real possibility, the solitary path of the body mystic is futile. Brown replied that Marcuse does not appreciate the vicious cycle of revolutions; Marcuse is not radical enough. History is a cycle of revolutions followed by a reinstitution of repression; the old revolutionaries become the new dictators. Breaking that cycle to create a truly new society requires a more radical revolution than Marcuse and the political radicals suspect: a revolution in the structure of the body and in the notion of reality that is rooted in this structure.*

The most difficult part of the Rolfing experience for most people is learning how to relate to their old environment with a new body. In the months during and after Rolfing, people find they must change their outer world: their jobs, marriages, relationships, values.

Between the body and the body politic lies the world of experience. My immediate experience (so omnipresent that it usually goes unnoticed) is of my body: hot and cold, hard and soft, right and left, balance and imbalance, pleasurable and painful, satisfying or disturbing, fearful or peaceful. On the basis of those rudimentary experiences, I assess my world. As I do so, I act, rejecting certain forms of activity and supporting others.

My body structure is mirrored in the history of my relation to the world outside my skin. I have what Fritz Perls called an "imploded" structure. The direction of energy is from outside in. I have lots of energy within myself, drawn from many sources throughout my life. But it has been extremely

* This debate originally appeared in *Commentary,* February and March 1967, and is reprinted in Marcuse's *Negations* (Boston: Beacon Press, 1968), pp. 227–247. Brown gave a longer reply in "From Politics to Metapolitics," *A Caterpillar Anthology,* ed. Clayton Eshelman (New York: Doubleday, Anchor Press, 1971), pp. 3–15.

difficult for me to let that energy flow with effectiveness into the world. During my first twenty years, I stayed almost completely inside myself, living much of the time in a world of daydreams and fantasies about a better life somewhere else. When I was twenty, I began to become aware of the critical problems in the world, and feelings of compassion for the oppressed were awakened in me. In my mind, I supported those groups who were trying to improve the conditions of the world, but my activity was that of a mystic and a scholar. In the sixties, the mental compassion grew into outrage, precipitated by the war in Vietnam. While I was experiencing the new inner spaces revealed by LSD and various body therapies, I made more tentative steps outward, joining the Resistance and participating in other radical groups. But I remained safely on their fringes. During the past decade, as I have worked more directly with the walls within my own body, I have experienced more ability to be in the world effectively. I have made some very modest steps out of my dreamworld into the hurly-burly world of other people.

"To perceive that it all really takes place in one body
is to transvalue the old political categories
to pass from politics to metapolitics
                    or poetry
The proletariat is dead
        but the proletariat is us
        long live the proletariat.
There is an inner Bastille to be captured
                    to release the prisoners
or rather, the inner and the outer Bastille is the same Bastille
or rather, the distinction between the inner and outer is the Bastille
                the false reality-principle
                the government of the reality-principle,
                    to be overthrown

And the revolution is a visionary break-through
                    or poetry.
                    or madness."*

After a very quiet session in which a Rolfer-friend had loosened the tissue around my left hip joint, I came back to my motel and cried for eight hours. I found myself engulfed in the image of gates opening inside myself. The gates seemed to be the two halves of my rib cage. When driving back to Santa Fe the next day along the Sangre de Cristo mountains, I could see so much more clearly. I was driven by a desire to insert myself directly into the world I was looking at.

Effective and valuable political action has at least these fundamental requirements: (1) it must proceed from knowledge, and (2) it must proceed. Both are functions of body structure.

The clear knowledge of what kinds of political structures are of service to the human community is rooted in the radical experience each of us has of the polity within. The microcosmic body is a political system. Your body is a political system that works or doesn't work, or works fairly well or poorly. We each have an immediate experience of how various different parts interact to produce a healthy or sickly organism. And by developing the kinds of consciousness suggested in this book, you can gain immediate experience of the mechanisms of increased or decreased functioning within the whole, as well as what constitutes optimum functioning.

Clear-headed knowledge of what "ought to be" isn't enough. Such knowledge has to be able to proceed into the world of effective actions. That is for many of us a major problem. Our energies are locked up inside our bodies. We are in such conflict that we are unable to participate with other like-minded people in constructing a more harmonious society. The blocks

* Brown, "From Politics to Metapolitics," p. 11.

to our energy can be found in the tight pectoral muscles, the atrophied extensors of the back, chronically contracted neck muscles, or a short psoas.

"Since it seems demonstrable that man's outer world is a projection of that which is within, is it not possible that some of the problems of our times might be resolved by examining the man himself, his physical being, his body? Could it be logical to suppose that if a way were found to organize better the actual physical structures of men, their outer confusions, mental and cultural, might lessen?"*

I am not espousing the theory that society is a collection of individuals. I am suggesting, on the contrary, that many of the ills of our culture are rooted in the illusion that we are atomic individuals. Even a sociologist or anthropologist who writes books on the individual as a creation of society may, in fact, experience himself as an atomic individual, radically separated from the larger world. I am suggesting further that the structure of the body is a radical factor in this illusory notion. As the flesh is cleared of its imbalances and tensions, the person experiences more unity with the larger world.

A young woman had just finished working with me on her head and neck. As she began to leave my studio, she stood frozen at the door with tears in her eyes. "I can't stand the thought of leaving this room. My old face covered what I was feeling and protected me from others. I don't want to have to expose myself to all that's out there."

Two major factors in the development of our body structures are protection and appearance. Most of us have developed our bodies to shield us from the experience of physical and emotional pain. Our body styles are designed

* Ida Rolf, "Structural Integration: Gravity, an Unexplored Factor in a More Human Use of Human Beings," *The Journal of the Institute for the Comparative Study of History, Philosophy and the Sciences* 1, no. 1 (June 1963): 3.

to make us look good (or frightful or cool or repulsive). Function is of minor concern. Few people give much attention to what is deeply useful for the body, what nourishes it at every level, what are the lines of real ease and comfort.

Protection and appearance are mirrored in our sociopolitical structures. Defensiveness and image-making hold the day. The greater part of our national budget is for military expenditures. The style of political leadership is to project the image of confidence and knowledge. Even the supposed nourishing activities of government—health, welfare, education—demonstrate the same lack of clarity that our personal body programs show. Just as we have little sense of how to take care of our bodies, so we have little sense of how to use our collective wealth to help the poor, to educate children, to support the aged, or to give medical assistance to those who need it.

When Ray appeared for his eighth session, it was snowing heavily. He reported experiencing nothing about his body during the week because he was too busy with schoolwork. However, for the first time in months he had not experienced any pain. The session went very simply. I worked mostly on his lower legs and feet, attempting to get more balance between the right and left sides of his body and more freedom of movement in his pelvis. His left side was shorter than his right, and I saw much of the shortness reflected in the rotation of the tibia and fibula in his lower left leg. He did, in fact, feel significant lengthening all the way along his left side and reported feeling much lighter all over.

The difficulty and the unique genius of Rolfing appear after the first seven sessions. It is relatively easy to learn to do the work of the early sessions: it is a matter of stretching what is short and of separating layers of tissue that have become matted and glued together. But once the body is in a loosened, flowing, and malleable state, it is ready to work with my hands to a new place of balance and ease. In the last three sessions of the basic Rolfing therapy, and in the advanced sessions, the goal is to integrate the body, guiding it into new movement patterns by moving the large fascial planes of the body in appropriate directions. "Appropriate directions." We move here from the familiar world of loosening, opening, freeing, and relaxing into a mysterious world of balanced movement. The unique aim of Rolfing is to serve the inner dynamics of the flesh that tend toward the fullness of bodily function in relation to the earth's field. The goal is not "openness," but freedom of choice.

The attitudes each of us holds toward the structure of our bodies is mirrored in our attitude toward political structure:

"That's just the way it is. It's always been that way and will stay that way."

"It's no good, but there's nothing I can do about it."

"It's just great." ("Since there's nothing I can do about it, why think about its inadequacies?")

"Well, things could be a little better. I can do a little bit here or there. But don't get too excited. There's not a whole lot I can do about it."

"Just let things run their course."

"I hate this thing and I'm going to work my ass off to change it."

Each of us has a fundamental bodily experience of order, intercommunication of parts in a system, energy flow and blockage, efficiency of movement within a system. Even the fundamental political notion of justice is partly rooted in our bodily experience of uprightness, balance, and the relation between the right and left sides of the body. If the experiences that ground our political thought are unclear (if, for example, we have only a vague perception of balance in our bodies), our political categories will be just as unclear.

There are confusions in the flesh that are the partners of mental confusions. If you've ever seen a dissected corpse, or a picture of one, you can notice that at certain places in the body the connective-tissue fibers are literally confused; there is no pattern in their directions. Instead of providing a clear channel of movement for their muscles, they distort, pulling the fibers in various directions. You can see and feel this confusion in the living body. Watch people walking in a crowded shopping mall. You'll see many instances of people not knowing quite what to do with their legs, how to swing their arms, or how to carry their weight comfortably. These fleshly confusions are writ large in the confused way we run our world.

Serious work on one's body involves serious commitment to larger social issues. It is impossible to think of improving the life of a personal body without improving the life of the body politic. Even if you were to run off to a mountain cave to become a hermit, you couldn't escape atmospheric pollution. And if you weren't blown off the face of the earth in time, your cave might someday be surrounded by condominiums.

When the thickenings in the fasciae investing our perceptual centers have been cleared away, we receive more data from our environment. We become more sensitive to the conflict, negativity, and pain that surround us. They are, after all, the reasons we developed the knots in the first place. We are then faced with various alternatives. One can, for example, withdraw from this insane world to live a bohemianlike existence isolated from its disturbing sensory input. Or one can continue the schizophrenic compromise of living in the world as it is, keeping one's secret to oneself to be shared with friends joining to get high by candlelight. Or one can begin to let one's inner ease expand outward to create a more nourishing environment for oneself, in the family, in the work situation, among one's friends, and still further into the larger arenas.

The theme of this chapter is at least as old as the classic Western work on politics, Plato's *Republic*. Plato constructed his analysis of the state on the analogy with the human being. Each element of the state corresponded to a part of the human person; each process and interaction of parts within the state's growth and decline corresponded to a process of growth or decline within the person. Paul used the human body as an analogy for explaining the structuture of the ideal Christian community. The alchemists used the body as the microcosmic entity whose analysis would yield knowledge of the macrocosmic universe. Freud traced the cultural history of mankind back to its roots in intrapsychic conflict, which Reich related directly to body structure. Some contemporary anthropologists, like the alchemists, claim that the structure of a given culture is revealed in the body patterns of any of its members.

"Logos seeks unification; and the fact it faces is Division
Alienation, in the old Marxist vocabulary
the rents, the splits, in the newer Freudian vocabulary
the schisms
the schizophrenia.
Now—if I may make a Great Leap Forward—
alienation is schizophrenia
the outcome of the collision between Marx and Freud is their unification
the perception of the analogy between the two
the analogy between   social and psychic
                          society and soul
                          body and body politic."*

This chapter is an exercise in metapolitics. It isn't an espousal, or a criticism, of any political system. It is a direction for you to take in meditating on the roots of any political system in your experience of your own body. But the meditation is dangerous; it is meant to change your mind and the world.

Wilhelm Reich has laid the groundwork for the beginnings of a more precise understanding of the relation between body structure and political structure. But at present, we are only at the threshold of useful knowledge.

* Brown, "From Politics to Metapolitics," p. 8.

The research done in recent years in social anthropology has contributed significantly to understanding the relation between the body and larger cultural forms. But even here, the studies are more on the side of what might be called the "postural" manifestations of the human body: nonverbal expressions, dance, costumery, ritual. There is no research into the deep structure of bodies in various cultures.

"While we have studied body styles, feather head-dresses, penis-sheaths, smiles, postures, earrings, tattooing, cranial deformation, gestures, etc.—we have studied each of these on its own. We have allowed our own condition of social anomie, of formlessness, to creep into our research and we have not given definite organic form and structure to the limits and definition of our subject. If we have failed to gain an understanding of the body as a whole system of meaning, then we have also failed to utilize the study of *corporal* form as a tool for the understanding of *social* form and hence we have failed to further our understanding of social systems and social bodies."*

I envision the development of a new science whose researchers would be educated in both structural anthropology and the sophisticated notions of body structure and kinesiology inspired by the work of Ida Rolf. The goal of this science would be an accurate understanding of the interrelationships between patterns of body structure in a given culture and the larger social forms of the culture. The practical goal would be to provide more clarity and power for those attempting to transform the culture by work on the body: medicine, various forms of therapy, architecture, furniture and fashion design, education, forms of exercise, sports, and the arts.

* Ted Polhemus, "Social Bodies," in *The Body as a Medium of Expression,* ed. Jonathan Benthall and Ted Polhemus (New York: Dutton, 1975), p. 33. This book is a good survey of recent work on these themes by social anthropologists and sociologists.

What many of us want is one body in which all the parts work together for the good of the whole, in which the interaction of whole and parts is mutually nourishing, in which the energy of the whole system is maximized, and in which there is ease of movement and pleasure. But how can we establish such a system unless we have experienced one?

Harmony, integration, unity: these are issues both for the individual and for the race. My history and that of the people whose stories I've told are filled with conflict. Johnny's tight pelvis protects him from the terror of letting go to the irrational forces of sexual energy. His tight muscles, which he developed to become a good athlete, attractive to women, and pleasing to his father, instead slow him down and drain his energy, making him unsuccessful as an athlete, unattractive to women, and a disappointment to his father. His emotions are torn between hating his parents and loving them to the point of absolute submission to their plans for him. His world is one of total conflict: people hostile to one another, classes in struggle, nations pouring all their money into military budgets. So what does unity or harmony mean? What possible empirical base can Johnny have for understanding what he would like to affect in his world?

The empirical base has to be constructed slowly from within. Johnny can be helped to the point where he can sense the movement initiated by each breath reach all the way down his legs to his arches and right up through the back of his head. He can learn to experience his body so that as he walks he feels an easy movement through the whole of his back from his tail bone up through the back of his neck to the base of his skull. As he seats himself, he can learn to sense how slight adjustments at his pelvis will help his head be easier and clearer, and how to allow his breath to keep his upper chest open for full oxygenation. It's indeed a modest, almost frivolous, beginning, a long way from the transformation of mankind, but the small beginning is one of the many factors necessary to break the endless cycle of human repression.

Even this small beginning reveals the interaction of personal and political action. If, for example, Johnny's parents become more sensitive to the needs of his body, they and other parents may want to change the physical structure of the school classrooms where he spends so much time. They may also want to change the kinds of food that are available in the cafeteria. They would soon discover, however, that both furniture and food contracts represent a vast industry closely tied in with the highest levels of state government. Neither the principal nor the local school boards have power in these areas, so the parents would be forced into politics at the state level. Johnny's parents also read many reports indicating that pollution of the environment is a major factor in health. As they become involved in groups whose aim is changing the destructive direction of heavy industry, they would find themselves at the level of national and international politics.

The perfection of human form is not something given us from the beginning. Maximizing body energy, creating utmost ease, resilience, and perceptibility within the upright posture, are the achievements of centuries within the race and decades within the individual life. So with political form. It's not a matter of going back to primitive origins, or to animal organizations, or of selecting existing alternatives. It's a matter of releasing our creativity, blasting out our old pictures of how things are.

The body politic is like the body of Proteus or those dancing bodies in my dream: a diaphanous, shifting, moving field of energy. There is nothing solid about it.

Is it too late? Are the forces of repression about to seize the day once and for all? We can sit around bitching and feeling guilty about our part in enhancing those forces, or we can step into the river. When I was beginning to learn the work from Ida Rolf, I said to her about the woman lying in front of me, "I don't know what to do now." She replied, "Just get your fingers in there and move."

8

Body and Spirit

In an interview (June 1970) with the Santa Cruz journal of opinion *The Free Spaghetti Dinner,* Norman O. Brown said: "The movement in *Life against Death* was certainly moving down into the body and finding the reality to be bodily. But after I had gotten there, another movement was set going which might be expressed this way: 'But the body when you find it is not just a body.' In Christian terminology, it's a spiritual body."

My central purpose in this book has been to dissolve the popular notion of the body as a clearly bounded, solid, unchanging individual object "out there." In the last chapter, I began to extend the limits of the personal body, reflecting on the intimate dance that goes on between what is inside your skin and what lies outside in the familiar world of sociopolitical structures. This chapter carries the assault on boundary thinking a long step further.

Where does your body end and mine begin? Where does the air that enters your lungs end and you begin? Are you different from the food and waste products in your system? What are the boundaries between you, your smells, and those who smell you; between the light emitted by you and the eyes that see you; between the sounds you emit and the ears that hear it; between the you who embodies thoughts on a page, the pen, the paper, and the person who reads your letter?

Although the skin is a convenient boundary for the purpose of ordinary discourse and action, is it any more *real* than the boundary constructed by a surveyor around your plot of land?

The commonsense notion of the body is that of a thing in space and time. That notion is an instance of the popular tendency to split mind and matter. To conceive of the body as an energy system is to conceive of it as interrelated with other systems. My experience at any given moment is of the series of interrelationships: the interaction of body, atmosphere, and food; the interaction of the central nervous system with sound, color, light, and gestalt; the interaction of memory, appetite, and instinct with the environment.

The "spiritual" is what is experienced when all the boundaries are experienced as arbitrary.

Some of the boundaries are obviously human constructions: property lines, national or state borders, the delineations between physics and chemistry. Some people, however, are seduced into thinking of these boundaries as natural or even divine. The boundaries I've been largely concerned with in this book are the boundaries found within the flesh: the walls we've constructed to protect us from the dangers outside our skin; the compensatory hardening in muscle groups to protect ourselves from feeling the pain of imbalance; the hardening of fascia that obscures the perceptual centers by setting up boundaries between my sensory receptors and stimuli.

Once, when Ida had done a session with me, spending most of the hour loosening and restructuring my sacrum, I walked out onto a dock in the Gulf of Mexico. *I* ceased to exist. I experienced being a part of the sea breeze, the movement of the water and the fish, the light rays cast by the sun, the colors of the palms and tropical flowers. I had no sense of past or future. It was not a particularly blissful experience: it was terrifying. It was the kind of ecstatic experience I'd invested a lot of energy in avoiding.

I did not experience myself as the *same* as the water, the wind, and the light, but as participating with them in the *same system* of movement. We were all dancing together. To experience all boundaries as conventional is not to experience everything as the same, but everything as interrelated.

The psychotic quality of this experience came from my fear, which itself was rooted deep in my flesh. Over the years, as my body has become more integrated, the same kind of experience is available without the terror.

Dorothy is a thirty-five-year-old, attractive, and intelligent science teacher. She was psychologically sophisticated, having participated in a number of groups and therapies. When she first came to be Rolfed, she complained a lot about her appearance. She often did that. She also often reported feeling very upset when another teacher or friend would ask her to explain Rolfing. Since she was unable to give them an adequate explanation, she doubted the validity of her own experience. As the Rolfing progressed, I noticed tremendous sadness in her. I was getting a strong feeling that her sense of self-worth came totally from outside and had little to do with her own experience of herself. One day she was so upset that she said she just wanted to talk and not to work. At one point, I found myself asking her what she felt about what people call the "spiritual." She quickly and firmly replied that she had given up any relation to that when she was eleven years old. I asked her if she had any realization of a level of her being that was simply OK, that just is, no matter what anyone thinks of it. Tears came pouring out along with a flood of memories, particularly of the death of her grandmother when Dorothy was four years old. She had been the only one who had communicated some sense of that feeling to Dorothy, and she hadn't lasted long. The misery of Dorothy's early years unfolded. As it did, she began to realize that she had used all her therapy to give her a more sophisticated knowledge of how shitty she and her fellow humans are. Gestalt had been used by her to give her a keen perception of her elaborate social games; Rolfing had been used to gain a deeper awareness of the subtle blocks and aberrations in her body.

It was clear that she had no sense of her self, her being. All that was real for her were her conditioned responses and social games. I felt that she would profit by giving energy and attention to a deeper layer of self through practicing some form of meditation. She reported that she had practiced transcendental meditation for a while. She spoke of her experience of it like everything else. She would get upset because it wasn't going right; she wasn't getting anything out of it; she didn't know how to do it. I suggested that she try it again, but from the space of simply allowing her self to be, just letting the mantra go on and observing whatever comes up, even if what comes up are restlessness and hassles. The suggestion was to allow herself just *to be* for a short time each day, to let her basic self-awareness begin to emerge.

In the middle of my session with Dorothy, I became more clear about the nature of spiritual expertise and its relation to other professional skills. There is an ancient body of knowledge about successful methods that have been developed to unlock the kind of self-awareness that Dorothy had blocked out when she was a child. There are people trained in that knowledge just as there are people trained in the skills of Gestalt therapy or Rolfing. Ida Rolf is a genius about matters pertaining to the physical body but has no special skill in matters pertaining to the spiritual and the emotional self. Carl Jung was a genius in unwinding the intricacies of the psyche; he was intelligent about the spirit but less than intelligent about the body. Swami Muktananda is a genius in opening the space for people to experience the spiritual; he is intelligent about the body and the emotions.

These questions will reveal for you your experience of the spiritual level of your existence: Am I ever able just to be with myself—not worrying about what I should be doing, about my problems, or about doing this exercise properly; not being upset because I'm uncomfortable or because I'm not getting what I expected from the exercise? Or if I am, in fact, worried and upset, can I just be with myself worried and upset? Can I just be in a comfortable position, breathing easily, allowing to emerge whatever is going on within myself without blocking any of it? Can I be aware of myself in such a way that I am just what I am, and that's OK? Do these questions even make sense to me?

The "spiritual" refers to the level of ultimate integration in ourselves, that level which makes sense out of all the other levels. When all the boundaries used to shape our world are experienced as arbitrary, we can experience the total system of interrelationships itself, the only unity that is not arbitrary.

There are many parodies of this level of existence. The most common and destructive in its ability to distract people from true spirituality is the notion that to be "spiritual" means to withdraw from the illusory world of matter, time, and history. In this view, the goal of being spiritual is attaining a bliss that can never be had in the hurly-burly world of economics, sex, and hunger. In this view, several boundaries are left still standing: there are the spiritual people and the unspiritual, there is matter and spirit, there is the true world of eternal bliss and the illusion of hungry people in Appalachia.

The practice of centering differentiates spiritual consciousness from sheer psychosis. The breaking down of boundaries that characterizes spiritual disciplines as well as many emotional and body disciplines is done in the context of maintaining an awareness of one's core being. For example, in the midst of an absolutely chaotic flood of images and fantasies, you are taught to sit quietly and breathe.

The ability to center is a function of body structure. Breathing exercises, hatha yoga, sophisticated postures of meditation, are all means to prepare the body to be centered in the midst of the dissolution of its ego-world. A central goal of Rolfing is to awaken the physiological center of the body, including the structures deep in the belly and the pelvis.

The bodies of psychotics often manifest a structure that inhibits experience of the physiological center: the pelvis, for example, is often so extremely tipped forward that little energy can flow through the whole body.

In such a body, when the flood of images comes, there is no sense of harmony or integrity anywhere in the realm of experience.

The protean form of this book, designed to manifest the protean form of the body, may seem fragmentary, often illogical, and to be coming apart at the seams. But there is a harmony in the fragments—not the harmony of a rigid logic but of interlocking and repetitive themes.

A test of true spirituality is the compassion for all existing beings arising from my experience that I am part of their suffering. It is a test put to their disciples by Jesus, the Buddha, and their co-workers throughout the centuries, the genuine spiritual masters. As long as I experience a barrier between me and the starving people of the world, or between me and the struggles of my parents, or between me and the stupidity of our politicians, I haven't experienced the spiritual dimension of reality.

"Religion" is not the same as the "spiritual." It may not, in fact, have anything to do with it in the concrete case. Religions are to the spiritual level of existence what political parties are to the sociopolitical level of the self. We are aware of needs to be part of a larger community, to be of service to the world. Political parties may or may not be of use in relating to those needs. Similarly, participating in a religious group or following specific religious practices may or may not contribute to one's experience of the spiritual dimension of existence.

It is a common experience for us body therapists that emotional factors can hinder the body work unless we deal with them directly. I'm working on a woman's belly. It's tight; nothing seems to be moving properly. I'm feeling uneasy and I notice that she seems a little strange. I ask what's going on. She says she's had a long history of men causing her pain. We talk for some time about our relationship in the work, until we become clear about the process between us. I return to find the tissue of her belly opening with my hands. Or every time I touch a man's neck, he jumps. I ask what's going on. He begins to sob, recounting all kinds of old sorrowful memories. I return to his neck and he works comfortably with my hands.

What is not so often noticed is that difficulties at the level of spirit can hinder body work. Dorothy is a typical example of that. She was ready to deal with the physical and emotional content of the body work, but her blocking of the spiritual level hindered the full integration of her flesh. The clarification of her connective tissue served only to make her a more well oiled pessimist.

Ray appeared for his ninth Rolfing session, his face filled with color and an unusually full smile. His parents had always driven him to my office, since they were worried that the sessions were too intense for him to be able to drive by himself. Today he was alone. Although he had experienced a couple of days of stomach flu during the week, he had run and played paddleball every day. There had been no pain at all. The night before, he had gone dancing until 4 o'clock in the morning. Today he had gone horseback riding for the first time in several months. His height, which had always been at least an inch shorter than his father's, hadn't changed since the sixth grade. Now, he reported with great joy, he was as tall as his father.

My goal in this session was to balance his shoulders and rib cage. Originally, his whole torso looked as if someone had taken it and twisted it slightly clockwise around his center. His eleventh and twelfth ribs, especially on the left side, were so distorted that in the early sessions I could barely locate them. The compression in his upper three ribs and the myofascial structures associated with the shoulder joints made it almost impossible for him to allow me to touch them. But this time, I found the lower ribs had, because of our earlier work, shifted to where I could easily work with them to coax them into a normal position. He allowed me to work deeply in the armpit structures, stretching the pectoralis minor and inducing more movement in the uppermost ribs. I also lengthened the tissues in his arms, with special attention to his right wrist, which he had badly damaged in an acrobatic accident. While I was working on his left forearm, he recalled having driven a nail through his right lower leg about four years ago. At the end of the session, his ribs and shoulders were fuller and more balanced. The new position of his thorax gave more freedom to his pelvis. His pictures again demonstrated significant change.

The session was light, easy, and full of joy. We laughed together a lot. Ida Rolf teaches that a unique kind of seeing is required in the last three sessions and in the advanced work. It flows from love, from being aware of our unity with the other person. I felt this love and unity with Ray, and found myself working within him, instead of from the outside.

He asked about continuing the Rolfing after his tenth session. I explained that the ten sessions of manipulation would be sufficient for him at this time. They would put his body into a new balance that would spontaneously evolve over the next several months. I suggested that he could profit greatly from structural patterning, which would teach him a specific sense of how to flow more fully with the new space we had released in his body.

The level of spirit is associated with the mystery of "up." A sense of being in harmony with the universe that comes from spiritual consciousness works hand in hand with the sense of lightness that comes from freeing and balancing the connective tissue. A body that is comfortable in the verticle doesn't seem to be a possibility without both factors.

The body systems of India and China, which are now finding verification in Western laboratories, see the body as an organization of energy at certain levels, sometimes called "chakras." Each chakra in a given person carries a high or a low level of energy in relation to other chakras. The various methods of meditation developed by spiritual masters in the East have as their goal opening the full energy available in each chakra and establishing a harmony among all the chakras, creating a flow of energy throughout the whole body, with the crucial opening being at the top of the head, the crown chakra. There are many people who have done a lot of psychological work and a lot of body work, including Rolfing, who do not communicate a sense of "up." The addition of specifically spiritual work, under a skilled master, can often enable one to appropriate more fully the freedom made possible by physical and psychological work.

I practiced various forms of meditation under the guidance of Western spiritual masters for twelve years. A lack I had experienced during those years began to clear up the first time I sat with a group of Zen practitioners and was instructed simply to sit quietly and watch my breath. That was in 1967. Since that time, I have done a great deal of body work and have continued to meditate under the guidance of Eastern masters. What I experience now is much more powerful because of the body work.

The West lacks a tradition of teaching the relation of the body to higher forms of consciousness. There is not a single type of meditation done in the East that is not done in the schools of Western spirituality: the repetition of short phrases (mantra); chanting; visualization of spiritual guides (Jesus, Mary, the saints); astral projection, particularly into biblical times; visualization of sacred objects (the cross, the blood of Jesus); listening to communications from holy beings; and simply sitting and watching, which was actually my principal practice for about ten years. What is radically different about Eastern methods is the attention given to the body and the material environment: the attention to body posture that is prepared for in India by the exercises of hatha yoga; the teaching of breathing awareness, both the elaborate practices of Hinduism and the simple practice of Zen; the tradition of sacred dance; the sophistication of the use of types of sound and energy focusing in chanting. Even though both traditions teach the ultimate irrelevance of the body, there is in the East a practical reverence for the body as the nesting ground for spirit. In the West, this reverence is largely theoretical.

That is strange when you realize that the most profound teaching of the relation between body and spirit is found in the Gospels. The meaning of the Jesus event, jealously guarded by the early Fathers of the Church against those who would spiritualize it, is that God became a body; in Jesus, divinity and humanity were manifested as one. John and Paul argue that the meaning for us of the existence of Jesus is that we are all one body. Over and over again, for centuries, in council after council, the Church emphasized that this is no metaphor: Jesus has a real flesh and blood *body*; we are one with him and each other in our bodily existence; the Church is a unity of bodies, with a life demonstrating its unity in bodily ways such as the concrete ritual of the mass, in which we eat bread and wine. Paul teaches that Christ revealed that we are one body and that our disunity is an illusion.

But bodies have penises, vaginas, and anuses. That was a little too much for folks like Saint Augustine. So just as vigorously as the early theologians defended the bodily reality of Jesus and of divinity itself, they argued that Jesus never used his "private parts," or "pudenda" ("shameful parts"), except for the necessities of elimination, and he was not brought into this world in the usual way, by the insertion of penis into vagina. In fact, he was born, according to the ancient teaching of the Church, without the rupture of Mary's hymen.

The talk about the body in the West has been very general and abstract. That is true not only of the Christian mystics but also of the alchemists. The Hermetic tradition puts a great deal of emphasis on the transformation of the body, but in fact there is no sophisticated teaching about how to go about the literal transformation of the flesh.

Also, the cultural milieu regarding the body in the Mediterranean world at that time was fairly primitive. Greco-Roman art reveals an image of the body that is gross and heavily armored. The closest thing to the sophistication of India is the teaching of the mystical sects of Judaism, particularly the Essenes. But even that teaching largely concerns bringing the body into line by fasting, purifying diets, and rigorous treatment. There is not the appreciation that the energy of the body provides energy for the spirit.

Spiritual teaching begins to develop in the origins of monasticism with Saint Benedict in the fourth century. It comes to its flowering in the twelfth through the fourteenth centuries. And there is almost no teaching about the body. There is always a teaching about purification, fasting, physical austerities, and keeping the body in appropriate postures for prayer. But the approach is negative, keeping the body from getting in the way.

My own relation to the body has gone through at least three phases. During the first thirty-two years of my life, I *thought* the body was unimportant—I wanted very much to think that because I didn't like my body—but it was in fact important. It hassled me all the time, giving me pain, making me feel inadequate, making me feel restless and dissatisfied. During the next nine years, beginning with an intense series of events including reading Norman O. Brown, taking LSD, going to Esalen, and being Rolfed, I began to think of the body as extremely important. During this period, my body continued to hassle me, but I was beginning to love it, to feel that it is beautiful. Yet I wanted very much to have a perfect body both to please Ida Rolf, who always gave me trouble about having my head too far forward, and in the spirit of my Jesuit days, to give a good example to my clients.

During a retreat with Swami Muktananda in 1975, I had an experience of the radical unimportance of the body. During meditation, he came up to me, grabbed the top of my head, and rubbed it vigorously. I was flooded with the realization: I am not my thoughts. I am not my restlessness. I am not this or that desire. I am not my body. The result of this experience is that my body doesn't hassle me so much any more. For the first time in my life, I feel it's all right if my body stays just the way it is. But the fact is that my body feels better than ever and is closer to the ideal of balance proposed by Ida.

The body is of no ultimate importance. What *is* of ultimate importance is love among us all. There are lifelong cripples and people with twisted bodies who are filled with love and whose lives have served humanity. There are people with balanced, flexible, and energetic bodies who are selfish and cruel. Work with the body is of ultimate significance only within the context of the larger energy fields of life, when it serves the more comprehensive goals of human existence.

The paradox of the body.
Muktananda teaches that the body is unimportant. Throughout his life, he has given sophisticated attention to his body. He has always practiced hatha yoga, followed a healthy diet, and taken long walks regularly. He gives similar attention to his physical environment. His ashram is spotless and beautiful. He is in the kitchen early each morning to supervise the day's cooking. There is never a doubt about his reverence for material reality.

I have a friend who belongs to a Kabbalist group that teaches the importance of the body. In his home, nothing is in order or cleaned up. He eats a poor diet, smokes a lot, and doesn't get much exercise. The man asked me how I, a Rolfer, could hang out with a swami who taught the unimportance of the body.

Ida once said: "You can't get beyond the body unless you free the body itself."

From another standpoint, the body is of ultimate importance. The body is a level of our energy field and, in some form or other, will be with us forever. There is no doubt about the teaching of Christianity: Jesus rose from the dead with his body; his mother ascended into heaven with her body, and their bodies are but pledges that our bodies too are immortal. Paul says the whole teaching of Christianity stands or falls on the validity of that belief.

From quite a different perspective, the Hindu and Buddhist traditions view the distinction between matter and spirit as illusory. The human body, then, participates in the eternal and unified reality of the cosmos, though in a transformed state.

That is, of course, conjecture, a dance in the face of death. The point of the conjecturing is to add another onslaught against the assumption that the body is a gross, solid, basically unchangeable chess piece in life's game.

Body, psyche, spirit, are all interacting systems within the person. They each represent a viewpoint, a level of integration, a kind of energy found within each of us. Personal health is a function of the harmonious operation of all three. If one fails, the other systems are blocked in their development.

There is a pattern I have observed in my work with my body and other bodies that is illustrated in my paraphrase of a Zen teaching. Before one begins the work, there is only the body, with its sinews, guts, and bones. When one enters upon the work, one discovers that the body is more than a body: it is a record of past history, it is filled with parents, ancestors, demons, and gods. When one proceeds well into the work, one discovers that there is just the body, with its sinews, guts, and bones.

One morning several years ago, Ida Rolf clumped into her living room at Big Sur where about twenty of us were assembled. "Word's going around Esalen that Ida Rolf thinks the body is all there is. Well, I want it known that I think there's more than the body, but the body is all you can get your hands on."

9

The Body, Sex, and Love

"To love is to transform, and be transformed. The lover must be flexible, or fluxible. There are a thousand shapes of women, their figures or *figurae*; the lover, like Proteus, will now melt into flowing water, will be now a lion, now a tree, now a bristling boar."*

The bodies in my dream danced together in perfect harmony. They could merge into one another, pass through each other, and separate, always keeping the harmony of movement. Their lack of solidity made their harmonious activity possible.

Love is made difficult insofar as we think of ourselves as solid and fixed.

Consider the image of the group dance. Insofar as my body is rigid and follows set and predictable patterns of movement, I am that much limited in my ability to become a synchronous member of the ever-shifting patterns of group movement. Watch a herd of antelope moving across the plains, a flock of geese flying above, or a school of fish. Their bodies are in harmony

* Norman O. Brown, "Daphne, or Metamorphosis," in *Myths, Dreams, and Religion,* ed. Joseph Campbell (New York: Dutton, 1970), p. 94.

both with the group and with the continual flow of stimuli from outside. At the sound of a gunshot, the heads of the antelope turn in concert and their white rumps swing in a unified wave as they move together away from the danger. As the geese approach a new pond, members of the flock begin to descend in undulating succession. Trout dart in and out under rocks and through cascades, each seeming to respond to particular stimuli, but keeping the rhythm of the others.

The rigidities in my body, which Wilhelm Reich called "character armor," make it difficult for me to move in harmony with the human dance. I am restless, tired, hostile, or just out of joint. I'm not sensitive to the many and continual shifts of rhythm around me.

Love is about harmony, being able to move with others. The previous chapters have been about the bodily barriers to moving with others. On with the dance.

My unique history, with its early traumata, its teachings from parents and other significant adults about the meaning of life, and my responses, produced a body that was unresponsive to the bodies of others. I don't mean sexually unresponsive: I would get an erection at the slightest touch. But I didn't respond to the whole body of other persons: their anxieties and pains, their affection, their wisdom and intuition—those messages which came from their guts and hearts as well as from their genitals and brains. For the first thirty-five years of my life, my energy was trapped in my head and my genitals. My exterior activity in the world was that of an intellectual; my inner life was filled with sexual fantasies, most of which I feared because of my religious commitments, only some of which I enjoyed. Orgasms and mind trips had a similar quality in those days. Both were very unrelated to other persons—just explosions of my volcanic energy stored up in these places, huge bursts of intellectual insights and of semen. They had little to do with love.

I thought about love a lot in those days and taught a lot about it, turning many of my students on to love as the meaning of life. But even when I was in the midst of people for whom I cared and was of service, I always felt barriers, always felt apart and alone, my eyes drifting abstractedly out the window. The hellish places in my early psychedelic trips always felt like being trapped forever in a dark tower walled off from anything outside myself.

Love involves whole bodies being present to one another, not just genitals to genitals, mouth to mouth, brain to brain, or hand to hand. Nor just exterior body to exterior body. Love means that I am able to relate harmoniously to the way you are now bodily.

All love, even the most spiritual love, is bodily. The body is the medium of communication. Even the love of ancestors, of Jesus and the saints, of the Buddha, and of God himself are bodily: the nourishing of this more abstract kind of love involves visualization, iconography, and meditation with the inner eye. The expression of this kind of love is found in bodily ritual and meditation.

I said I was *trapped* in my genitals and head. That quality of my life was directly related to my body structure. The only places in my body I had much feeling were my head, neck, and genitals. As I have unwrapped my body during the past years, I have discovered that my genitals were literally walled up: the fascial coverings of the various muscle groups around the pelvis were thick and congested, allowing little feeling to pass from the genitals into the rest of my body, from the rest of my body into my genitals, or back and forth between my genitals and my lover's. Physiologically, my genitals were like a being apart from the rest of me, having their own will, which was a source of danger and terror. Similarly with my head: it was cut off from the rest of my body by a neck that was so tight that some of its muscles felt like bones. My life was a continual battle between my head, which wanted to spout off ideas about goodness and truth, and my genitals, which wanted to spout off semen. My heart remained buried in that no-man's-land in between.

"Union and unification is of bodies, not souls. The erotic sense of reality unmasks the soul, the personality, the ego; because soul, personality and ego are what distinguish and separate us; they make us individuals, arrived at by dividing till you can divide no more—atoms. But psychic individuals, separate, unfissionable on the inside, impenetrable on the outside, are, like physical atoms, an illusion; in the twentieth century, in the age of fission, we can split the individual even as we can split the atom. Souls, personalities, and egos are masks, spectres, concealing our unity as body. For it is as one biological species that mankind is one . . . so that to become conscious of ourselves as body is to become conscious of mankind as one."*

To become conscious of ourselves as body is to become conscious of mankind as one. In the world of ideas, fantasies, and emotions, it is easy for me to think of myself as separate from you. I don't know what you're thinking or feeling, even if you tell me, because the meaning of your words may differ from the meaning I attach to them—or you may be lying. But at the bodily level, my eyes are filled with you. Your sounds penetrate my ears. Our energy fields interact and make of us an interlocking system. We may even touch. Moreover, we both breathe the air surrounding us. We are moving in the same field of gravity. If you explore with care the bodily reality of our life, it is difficult to maintain the illusion of separateness.

Love involves the realization at every level of our being—mind, heart, guts, genitals—that the subsystems of unity are mind-made conventions that are as real as they are useful. The unity of the circulatory system, of the molecule, of the brain, of the earth, of you and me, are ways of speaking, of doing research, and of ordering our everyday worlds. Once again, they are tools for unlocking the meaning of things; they are not pictures of

* Norman O. Brown, *Love's Body* (New York: Random House, 1966), p. 82.

144

reality. There is one system of which the circulatory, the molecular, the nervous, the geophysical, the solar, and the personal systems are but members. Love is the unity of that system.

Love is not something to be attained; it is the reality in which we exist. What is necessary is conversion, realization, enlightenment.

I can operate from the viewpoint that I am me, you are you, the earth is the earth, and that's the way it is. I can conceive of myself as the lonely warrior traveling across a hostile land, meeting now and then for a brief moment a fellow traveler. When the body is out of harmony with the field of the earth, when the parts of the body are out of harmony with each other, and when one body is physiologically walled off from other bodies, such a viewpoint makes a lot of sense. But the dissolving of the walls reveals another possibility.

Love is not a feeling, an emotion, or an affection. It is the attitude and behavior of a person living by another viewpoint. The viewpoint is the realization that the referents of the words "I," "you," and "the earth" are elements within a single unified system of energy. The path into the body is a path into that realization. The more one follows the explorations only suggested in this book, the more one finds the whole universe.

The objection can be raised: Can't someone love specific others without realizing that everything is part of a single energy system? Aren't you legislating what is the correct view of the world and who really experiences love? Can't love exist as a feeling or emotion without that view?

Of course, persons love other persons, children love their pets, people love beautiful objects and their countries. But what is the basis for those experiences; what makes them even possible? More to the point, why is it that love is such an ineffectual force both in individual lives and in the life of the human community? My observations are about that aspect of reality which makes it possible for us to sense unity with another person, a group or country, or a beautiful work of art, an aspect that, when forgotten or unrecognized, befouls these primitively felt relationships.

To become conscious of ourselves as body is to become conscious of mankind as one. The world is screaming this lesson in our ears: the pollution of the environment, world famine, and the possibility of nuclear war are three major reminders that we exist bodily and are interconnected.

As the Light Princess discovered, there can be no love without gravity. To operate from the viewpoint of love means being sensitive to the teachings of the earth's field. Neglect of her universal presence contributes to the disintegration of the body, which in turn makes it more difficult for the body to perceive its relations to what is outside itself. Responsiveness to her teaching is a path toward a new harmony.

Presence to the other is essential for love's nourishment. But presence requires a body that is aware.

I used to be plagued by the experience of being with people yet not being with them—not really listening to them or perceiving them. I would be off in my own fantasies and thoughts all the time. I have discovered a bodily counterpart within myself to that separateness. The freeing of my flesh has literally opened up my perception. My overall experience is that I am less locked up within myself and more aware of the other; I receive more data from outside on many levels.

It's not merger with others that is the ideal, but the ability to merge when one chooses. I had created a body that protected me from that option. It is of value to be able to give oneself fully to sex, or to intellectual activity. Not valuable is the lack of options to pass at will from one kind of activity to another and, when appropriate, to experience several kinds of energy harmoniously within ourselves.

Sex is at its best from the standpoint of freedom. When I make love with my whole being—my pelvis, my legs, my head, my mind, my heart, my spirit—sexuality is of equal value with the most intense mystical experiences, precisely because it reveals our true nature: that we are parts of a blissful, ever-moving and -changing, energetic whole.

Wilhelm Reich explored how the uniqueness of our character is revealed in our experiences of lovemaking. If you sort out the distinct qualities of your own experience, you'll find out all you need to know about yourself.

Just from the viewpoint of the physical body, sex can involve only the insertion of penis into vagina, with ejaculation for the man and nothing for the woman. Or it can involve heavy, fast, voluntary movements of the whole body, with explosive orgasms centered mostly in the genitals. Or subtle, articulated, rhythmic movements of the whole body, involving deep breathing, culminating in a wavelike orgasm that engulfs the whole being. The latter kind of movement is often accompanied by involuntary motions of the body before orgasm. Different patterns of breathing accompany each of these styles.

Notice the variations in your awareness of the other person in your different types of sexual experience. Sometimes the body of the other person serves only to release my own pent-up energy in orgasm. At other times, my mind drifts off to everyday thoughts or fantasies. Or I express conflict and hostility in being aggressive and rough. Sometimes I feel tremendous affection for my lover and am aware of her whole being. Or I lose all sense of myself and her and feel only pure energy and bliss.

To become conscious of ourselves as body is to become conscious of mankind as one. This kind of unitive experience in sex comes from being fully conscious of my body, totally aware of it. The more I am aware of my body, the more I am aware of the other person and the world.

Lovemaking is a powerful teacher. In our bodies, it will reveal where we're not flowing and easy; in our intentions, it will teach us where our most fundamental energy separates us from what is outside ourselves—our lover and the universe.

I was doing an advanced Rolfing session on a friend. Whenever we would get to a difficult place in his body, all the muscles in the back of his neck and upper shoulders would dramatically contract, transmitting rigidity through his whole body. "That's what always happens to me when I'm about to come. It makes orgasms so painful."

I was working on a woman's knees. She kept tightening her belly as if someone were punching her there. "I always tighten there when I'm making love. I don't like doing that."

There was a lively debate during the Middle Ages in Europe about whether the knowledge or the love of God was the ultimate goal of human life. The debate divided whole faculties and universities. It even caused a number of street brawls in Paris and Oxford. Depending on your position regarding the question, you would join one religious order (say, the Franciscans) rather than another (say, the Dominicans), and would follow different spiritual disciplines.

With his customary synthetic genius, Thomas Aquinas wrote that both are elements of a total experience that mankind seeks. Knowledge, however, is the primary constituent, in that without realization there can be no love. The fruit of realization and awareness, he argued, is love.

But we are already in love. "The rents, the tears, splits and divisions are mindmade; they are not based on the truth but on what the Buddhists call illusion, what Freud calls unconscious fantasies."* This book is an exercise in challenging the illusions about the nature of the body that contribute to thinking we are not in love.

Ray's final session of Rolfing was uneventful. He said that he had been feeling better than ever during the three weeks since his last session. His weight had gone up from 115 to 135 pounds. The only difficulties he reported were tension in the back of his neck when he jogged and an unusual knee problem. He had awakened at midnight the previous Monday to find his knee all swollen and so painful that he couldn't bend it. The day before,

* Ibid., p. 81.

he had taken a brisk four-mile walk. The pain lasted until Wednesday and disappeared. (It hasn't recurred, and its source remains a mystery.)

As I worked quietly through his body, we both commented on how things had changed over the nine weeks. I was working more deeply than ever, but he was able to accept the work and the pain without resistance, quietly moving with my hands to complete the final level of balancing.

My work centered primarily on getting more length in his legs, more width in his upper back, and more movement in the hinge between his neck and the base of the skull.

As we examined the whole set of photographs at the end of the session, we noticed that along with the dramatic changes in the length and expansiveness of his structure, there had been a steady growth toward softness in his flesh: the early tenseness in his face and tightness in his shoulders and belly were beginning to disappear. His voice had become soft and deep.

We parted simply. He had begun patterning with Elissa and intended to continue with that. I advised him not to think of any more manipulation for several months unless he had an acute problem. Between the change in structure achieved in the ten sessions and the changes from the patterning, there would be a good deal of spontaneous evolution in his body during the next months, not to be interfered with.

There were times that I regretted selecting Ray's experience of the ten sessions of Rolfing to write up for this book. His case is one of the least dramatic. It involved no obvious changes in the way he related to the world outside his own body. But I realized the appropriateness of his case. It is very typical of the uniqueness of the Rolfing process and of the implications of the pure work with body structure. Many of the other stories I could have told could also have been told by any therapist or teacher of consciousness. But for a greater number of people, the gateway to expanded consciousness is this simple work with the body. Many of my clients are, like Ray, ordinarily healthy people whose lives work well enough. They would not think of going to a psychotherapist, or participating in est, or of meditating. But they might have some body discomfort, feel sexual problems, or just feel the effects of aging. So they undertake Rolfing. As the gates of their body open, they begin to experience new possibilities within themselves, new ways of looking at their lives. They begin to realize that they are much more than they thought they were and often take the steps necessary to realize that "more."

The pain in Ray's physical life has been greatly diminished. He has learned to love and respect the needs of his body more. He seems gentler and more able to respond.

"Inside" and "outside" are lies. An objection often raised about Rolfing is that it cannot be of real significance because it comes from outside the person and significant change must come from within.

My first response is that Rolfing, as well as any effective teaching, in fact takes place only within the person. My hands are the person's tools. I just work with the inner lines of energy dictated by the person's own rhythms.

But there is a lie here. It is that I am other than my client. From that standpoint, air is outside us, as are food, books, and the living teachings of Gurdjieff and Muktananda. From that standpoint, there is nothing within me, and no nourishment would be possible. The truth in the lie is that, from the standpoint of division, nothing significant can happen because to operate from that standpoint is to contribute to the lie. The genius of Muktananda, for example, is his ability to communicate that he is not other than me.

"The goal of psychotherapy is psychic integration; but there is no integration of the separate individual. The individual is obtained by division; integration of the individual is a strictly self-contradictory enterprise, as becomes evident in the futile attempts of the therapists to define 'what we mean by mental health' in the individual person. The goal of 'individuation,' or of replacing the ego by the 'self,' deceitfully conceals the drastic break between the *principium individuationis* and the Dionysian, or drunken, principle of union, or communion, between man and man and between man and nature. The integration of the psyche is the integration of the human race, and the integration of the world with which we are inseparably connected. Only in one world can we be one. The inner voice, the personal salvation, the private experience, are all based on an illusory distinction."*

The vow made by Buddha not to attain enlightenment until all sentient beings were ready for enlightenment was not a special act of love and courage: it was a clear recognition of the ways things are. If any part is out of harmony, the whole system is askew.

To become conscious of ourselves as body is to become conscious of mankind as one. As I become more deeply aware of my own bodily reality, opening the doors of perception, I perceive more about bodily reality around me. But the bodily reality around me is filled with pain, conflict, hunger. There is the birth of compassion, the awareness of the profound pain afflicting the body of mankind, and the urge to participate in its healing.

The only pleasure in life the Light Princess was able to enjoy was swimming in the lake in front of her palace. In the lake, she became nearly like other human beings. One day, a prince from another land came upon her in the lake and fell in love with her. But, although she enjoyed swimming with him, she could not understand his talk of love. One day, the wicked aunt, who had originally stolen her gravity, tired of seeing the princess enjoying herself in the lake. So she created from a piece of seaweed a huge snake that began sucking water out of a hole in the bottom of the lake. She also cast her magic potion in all the streams, drying them up. The princess was grief-stricken and retired to her palace, unwilling to watch her beloved lake dry up. The disguised prince offered himself to the king to plug the hole in the lake if only the princess would sit by him as he died drowning in the

---

* Ibid., pp. 86–87.

waters that would rise around him. The princess sat in a rowboat next to him as the waters slowly rose over his body, not paying much attention to him, only concerned that her beloved lake was again appearing. But as the waters reached his mouth and nose, she was suddenly struck with concern for the first time in her life. She dove into the water, pulled him out of the hole, and dragged his almost dead body to shore. She began to cry, realizing her love for the prince who had loved her so much that he was willing to die for her. She suddenly regained her gravity as the prince awoke.

The viewpoint of love is not arrived at by study but by our experience of people who relate to us from that viewpoint. I have learned of love from the people in my life who have approached me out of love. At a crucial time in my life, for example, when I was acutely aware of my life being locked in my genitals and my head, I met Elissa and I felt my heart open and experienced my whole body.

The path of love is not easy. We have not been stupid in armoring ourselves. The world is filled with hostility and threats to our integrity. Shedding our armor exposes us to more than bliss; it exposes us to a world in which emotional, spiritual, and physical dis-ease hold sway. The woman who killed herself the night before I began writing this book had lost her armor. What was outside/inside was too terrifying for her to bear.

The truth—love—speaks for itself. It doesn't need to be explained, forced, or sold. Whatever needs to be explained, forced, or sold isn't love. Explaining love is like explaining what it is to open one's eyes. The point is to open one's eyes.

Appendix

These final pages are meant to leave you with some specific information about how you might further what you have gotten from this book.

1. While this book was being published, Ida Rolf's own book was released: *Rolfing: The Integration of Human Structures*, published privately in California and available from The Rolf Institute, P.O. Box 1868, Boulder, Colorado 80302. It includes four hundred anatomical drawings done by an artist who worked with Dr. Rolf for several years to visualize her concepts.

2. Dr. Jim Polidora of the University of California at Davis has compiled a thorough bibliography of books about the body, giving a useful comment about each one. You can find literature on all the available body therapies, along with books of a more general metaphysical or psychological nature. There are also books about subjects like diet and exercise. The bibliography can be gotten by sending $2 to Dr. Jim Polidora, P.O. Box 709, Davis, California 95616.

3. Two other pieces of literature that will provide you with a lot of information about various ways to expand consciousness is the Esalen Catalogue, available from Esalen Institute, Big Sur, California 93920; and *The New Age Journal,* 32 Station Street, Brookline, Massachusetts 02147.

4. An introductory book for developing a concrete health program is Dr. John McCamy and James Presley's *Human Life Styling: Keeping Whole in the Twentieth Century* (New York: Harper & Row, 1974). The book is excellent both because of the reliability of its simple programs and because it combines several aspects of health—exercise, diet, stress reduction, and politics.

5. A simple and very useful book to gain a more specific understanding of the kind of movement I've discussed throughout this book is Timothy Gallwey's *The Inner Game of Tennis* (New York: Random House, 1974).

6. You can obtain a list of Rolfers and structural patterners along with more literature on both from The Rolf Institute, P.O. Box 1868, Boulder, Colorado 80302.

7. As I got to the end of the book, I realized that a former teacher of mine was lurking in the wings throughout: Bernard Lonergan, S.J., author of one of the great philosophy books of the age: *Insight: A Study of Human Understanding* (London: Longmans, Green, 1961). Lonergan helped liberate me from what he calls "naïve realism," the notion that the "real" is the "already out there now" and that ideas are pictures of those real objects out there. This cleaning up of my mind prepared me for my later meetings with Norman O. Brown and Ida Rolf. *Insight,* which I recommend for those of you who are metaphysically inclined, is a long and sustained training in reflecting on our experience of experience, forming ideas, making judgments and decisions.

8. There's an adage about the spiritual life that says, "You don't pick your teacher; your teacher picks you." There is a proliferation of books on, and teachers of, the spiritual dimension. If you are open to the possibility of this dimension within yourself, you'll find, by trial and error, what's useful for you. A book that I've found useful in discerning between good and bad spiritual teaching is Chogyam Trungpa's *Cutting through Spiritual Materialism* (Berkeley, Calif.: Shambhala, 1973).

9. In July 1976, *Co-Evolution Quarterly* sponsored a conference on mind-body dualism under the leadership of Gregory Bateson and Stewart Brand. The papers of the conference, which appear in the *Quarterly* beginning with the Fall 1976 issue, are relevant to the themes of this book. One in particular relates to my own philosophical position: Francisco Varela's "Not One, Not Two," *Co-Evolution Quarterly,* no. 11 (Fall 1976), pp. 62–67.